"Aren't you afraid Mario will hate you?"

"I don't doubt he'll be a little angry at first." Santino sounded faintly amused as he answered her question. "But Mario has family obligations, and I'm sure he will be glad to know that you're being—well looked after."

"By you, I suppose," she said, her voice shaking with anger. "If you only knew how I hate you."

He laughed. "It doesn't particularly disturb me, *bèlla mia.*" He bent his head and she felt his breath warm on her neck. "Don't let's fool ourselves, Janina," he muttered thickly. "There was something between us from the moment we saw each other. I knew it and so did you, so we'll forget the virtuous denials."

Juliet was close to panic. It would be so easy to turn to him, to yield....

Other titles by

SARA CRAVEN
IN HARLEQUIN PRESENTS

Other titles by

SARA CRAVEN
IN HARLEQUIN ROMANCES

SARA CRAVEN

moth to the flame

Harlequin Books

TORONTO · LONDON · NEW YORK · AMSTERDAM
SYDNEY · HAMBURG · PARIS

Harlequin Presents edition published September 1979
ISBN 0-373-70807-6

Original hardcover edition published in 1979
by Mills & Boon Limited

CHAPTER ONE

'WELL, I can't understand you,' Mrs Laurence said plaintively. 'Most girls would give their eye teeth for a week in Rome with all expenses paid.'

Juliet Laurence repressed a sigh and gave her mother a look of affectionate resignation. 'You make it all sound so simple,' she said.

'It is simple,' her mother protested.

'And of course Jan will welcome me with open arms, without the slightest idea that I've been sent out to spy on her.'

'What an unpleasant way of expressing it!' Mrs Laurence directed a quelling glance at her older daughter. 'That is not my intention at all. I admit that I'm concerned, but ...'

'But you want to know what she's doing, and why she hasn't written to you for nearly a month, without actually asking her directly,' Juliet supplied accurately.

'But she never keeps me waiting so long for a letter,' Mrs Laurence said defensively. 'Something's wrong, I know it is. I have one of my feelings ...'

'Oh, Mim!' Juliet smiled ruefully. 'You and those "feelings" of yours—the panics they've started! If you're so worried, why don't you telephone Jan? It would be cheaper than sending me to Rome to ferret out the information for you.'

'I can't phone her. I'd sound like one of those dreadful, over-protective mothers who keep dragging their fledglings back to the nest,' Mrs Laurence said fretfully. 'Jan would hate it. And I've never pestered or interfered, have I?'

Juliet patted her hand. 'No, Mim, love, of course not.'

And if the thought fleetingly occurred to her that if it had been herself all those miles away in Rome instead of her younger sister, her mother's antennae might not have been quite so sensitive to impending doom, she loyally suppressed it. After all, Jan was her last-born, and Juliet had always known, ever since her sister's birth, that Jan was the favourite child. It was an instinctive knowledge and she had been able to absorb it without particular hurt, because she knew that she was also loved and valued, and that what favouritism there was had been wholly unconscious on her mother's part.

Jan, after all, was everyone's darling. She was incredibly lovely to look at, for one thing. Strangers had hung over her pram, cooing rapturously while she accepted their homage. She had continued to accept it all through her childhood, at school and at play, and no one had been in the least surprised when a career in modelling beckoned when she was seventeen. And now she had been working in Rome for almost a year at a leading fashion house, the latest in a series of glamorous jobs.

Juliet did not grudge her sister one iota of her almost meteoric success. No one, she had realised a long time ago, was ever likely to offer her a career in modelling, even if that had been what she wanted—unless it was to advertise tights or nail varnish. Her legs were long and shapely, and her hands small and well cared for, but her figure, although slender and rounded in the right places, would never set the world on fire, she thought judiciously, and while she shared Jan's basic colouring, her own hair tended towards a bright copper rather than her sister's rich red-gold colour and her eyes had more grey than green in them. Her face was thinner, too, its cheekbones more prominent and the mouth more vulnerable.

It was odd to think of herself as the more vulnerable when she was the older by eighteen months. When they had been small, she had always been protective towards Jan, alert for the sort of mischief that could lead to danger. Jan had seemed to accept this in much the same spirit as she received admiration, but at the same time she seemed to have been born knowing exactly where she was going and what she wanted out of life, whereas Juliet had never really known where her path would lead. It had led, eventually, to training as a teacher, and she had just completed her probationary year. She was happy and settled in her post in a primary school, but was that really how she should be feeling at twenty-two? she wondered. She had never let the knowledge that Jan regarded her as a stick-in-the-mud worry her in the past, because she had never craved the sort of limelight that seemed to be her sister's life's blood, but just recently she had begun to ask herself whether Jan's strictures might not have a certain justice, and whether she was not in grave danger of resigning herself to a rut.

There was Barry Tennent for one thing. He taught at the same school, and they had been out together several times. Juliet admitted that she enjoyed his company, and she knew that Barry was ambitious, with his eye on a deputy headship before he was thirty. Nor did she find him unattractive. But was that really all there was to it—to marry a man because his prospects were sound, and he was 'not unattractive'? Her mother too approved of Barry. She said he was 'reliable' as if that was the one quality that mattered, but Juliet was not so sure. It was all so safe and so humdrum.

She had even found herself guiltily wishing of late that it could be possible to change identities with Jan just for a brief while so that she could see what another lifestyle was like. But there was no profit to be gained from that kind of daydreaming. Perhaps a change of job would provide the impetus she needed. She could even work abroad. A girl she had been at college with was now living with a family in one of the E.E.C. countries, teaching their children English. Perhaps Katie might know of a similar post that would appeal to her.

It was this feeling of restlessness which had sorely tempted her to agree without a second thought when her mother had first suggested the trip to Rome—and if the invitation had come from Jan herself, she would not have hesitated. But Jan had never suggested that either her mother or her sister should visit her in her adopted city. She came home, of course, bringing generous presents—beautiful handbags and belts, and delicious perfume, and tossing them casual stories of parties she had attended and celebrities she had met, but her visits were never long. Jan, Juliet thought dispassionately, bored easily. She always had, even as a small child. She could remember incidents in childhood play, and even friendships disrupted by Jan's demand for novelty. It was almost surprising that her interest in her new career had not waned. Juliet had half-expected the glamour of that to pall after a few months.

She rarely heard from Jan, but as long as her mother received regular correspondence, she did not allow it to worry her too much. Her affection for her sister now was not quite so uncritical as it had been when they were younger.

Only now there had been no letters for over three weeks, and Mrs Laurence had reacted sharply to the prolonged silence.

Poor Mim, Juliet thought, stealing her a compassionate look. She had always tried so hard to seem impartial, and she would have been genuinely horrified if anyone had suggested that she favoured Jan more in any way.

'Mim,' she said gently, 'we really must leave Jan to live her own life, you know. There could be any number of reasons why she hasn't written lately. Perhaps she's extra busy just now, or away on a trip . . .'

'Or ill.' Mrs Laurence's eyes sought Juliet's. 'Oh, darling, something's wrong. I can feel it—here.' She pressed a hand to her breast.

'Nonsense,' Juliet said robustly. 'If she was sick then the Di Lorenzo company would have let you know. You would have been sent for.'

Her mother's hand reached for hers. 'Please, Juliet, go and see her. Put my mind at rest. If there is something the matter, she's more likely to confide in you than she is in me.'

'I wouldn't count on that.' Juliet's tone was dry. 'She's never been a great one for confidences, you know.'

'But you're her sister. Who else would she confide in?' Mrs Laurence looked a little hurt. 'Juliet, you sounded for a minute as if you didn't—love Jan.'

'Oh, I love her,' Juliet said calmly. 'And I'm just as be-witched, bedevilled and bedazzled as everyone else who comes within her aegis. But to be honest, Mim, there are moments when I don't actually—like her very much, and when she upsets you just happens to be one of them ... However, if it will please you and give you some peace of mind, I'll go to Rome as soon as term ends. But you must write to Jan and tell her I'm coming. I won't just land on her unannounced. And if she replies that it's not con-venient, then wild horses won't drag me anywhere near Italy, and you must accept that.'

'Agreed,' Mrs Laurence said joyfully. 'And of course she'll want you, dear. It will be lovely for you, apart from anything else. You've been looking tired lately, and a nice break in the sun will do you good. Why, Jan might even ask you to stay on for a while.'

'She might,' Julie acceded rather wryly. She was men-tally running her wardrobe under review, wondering what it contained that would not look out of place in a high Roman summer. It would probably be very hot, she thought, so cottons would be preferable to synthetic fibres. One long skirt as well, maybe, and a couple of tops to wear with it in case Jan took her out on the town. In spite of her misgivings, a sense of excitement was beginning to pervade her. She'd only ever been abroad on school visits, and never to Italy. It would be a new experience for her—something to shake her out of that rut she was imagining.

Her feeling of anticipation intensified as the term drew to its close. Mrs Laurence had written to Jan as promised, explaining that Juliet needed a holiday and giving details of the flight she would be catching.

If Jan replied at the last moment cancelling the visit, it would be a terrible anti-climax, Juliet thought as she packed her lightweight case the evening before the flight. She had bought herself a few new things—some cotton jeans among them, and a couple of pretty shirts with long sleeves for sightseeing round Roman churches, as well as a long dress she hadn't been able to resist, but she was not taking many clothes. In spite of her mother's optimistic remarks about the possibility of a longer visit, Juliet doubted whether she would in fact remain in Rome for more than a week.

The very fact that Jan had not replied at all to her mother's letter seemed vaguely ominous. Juliet found herself wishing that there had been at least a perfunctory note acknowledging that she was expected, even if not as welcome as the flowers that bloom in the spring.

And certainly the continued silence had made her mother jumpier than ever about the whole situation, so that she had found herself promising devoutly to phone her the very evening of her arrival to let her know what was happening.

She had also received an alternative invitation to make up a party with some of the other teachers at the school, cruising some of the inland waterways on a barge, and in many ways this sounded far more appealing than a trip to Rome in the height of summer to visit a recalcitrant and

possibly resentful sister who was far more capable of
organising her life than Juliet herself would probably ever
be.

There was probably nothing more sinister behind her
failure to write home than mere thoughtlessness, Juliet
thought wryly as she locked her case, but there was no way
she would ever convince her mother of this.

Her misgivings returned with renewed force when there
was no one to meet her at the airport, or even a message
giving her directions how to reach Jan's apartment. She had
the address, of course, and she was perfectly capable of
finding the bus into the city and then picking up a taxi to
take her to her final destination, but it wasn't the same, and
she could not help feeling just a little hurt during the drive
into the city.

In other circumstances she would have been on the edge
of her seat, taking in all the ancient splendours around her.
As it was, she sat hunched rather tensely in a corner of the
taxi, her fingers curled tightly round the strap of her handbag. It had occurred to her for the first time that there
could be a good and valid reason why Jan had not responded to the news of her arrival. Perhaps she was away on
a prolonged trip, and had never received their mother's
letter at all. If that was the case, Juliet would really be in
the soup. Both she and Mrs Laurence had taken it for
granted that she would be staying at Jan's apartment and
they had not included the price of a hotel, even if she could
find a vacancy at this time of year, in their costs for the trip
which had necessarily to be kept to a minimum. Juliet had
not permitted her mother to pay the whole bill as she had
wanted, although she had accepted a little financial help
with the price of the air-fare. If Jan was away, then all her
careful budgeting would fall in pieces.

'*Ecco, signorina,*' the taxi-driver announced over his

shoulder, breaking into her troubled reverie.

Juliet leaned forward, staring up with disbelieving eyes at the tall building outside which the taxi had stopped. It wasn't at all what she had expected. In some of Jan's early letters, she had described amusingly the small flat over a greengrocer's shop in a square which she shared with another girl. When she had announced later that she had moved, Juliet had assumed that it was to a similar apartment, but it seemed that she could not have been more wrong.

Summoning what few Italian phrases she knew, she asked the taxi-driver haltingly if he was sure there was not some mistake. She did not understand all that he said in reply, but his air of grievance was easily recognisable, and when she produced the scrap of paper with Jan's address on it, he almost snatched it from her and stabbed at it with a pudgy forefinger. It appeared that if there was some mistake, it was not of his making. He had brought her to the address she had requested. She paid him, adding what she hoped was a reasonable tip to compensate his injured feelings, then walked up the wide marble steps to the glass swing doors of the apartment block.

The foyer was not over-large, but it was cool with air-conditioning, and a mosaic-tiled floor. A swarthy man in a dark red uniform sat in a glass-fronted cubicle to one side, and as Juliet with her suitcase hesitated for a moment, looking round for the lift, he waved a peremptory hand at her, obviously indicating that she should wait until he had finished putting through a call on the switchboard in front of him.

When he was ready, he looked her over from head to foot. '*Sí, signorina?*' There was a faint insolence in his tone which Juliet resented.

She said quietly. '*Scusi, signore, non parlo italiano.*'

'I speak English good, *signorina*. What you want I do for you?'

She said rather uncertainly, 'I'm looking for my sister. This is the address I was given, but I'm not sure ...'

'What name, this sister, and what apartment?'

Silently she handed him her scrap of paper. He studied it for a moment and his brows cleared.

'*Naturalmente, signorina.* The *signorina inglese* on the fourth floor. She did not speak to me that you were to arrive. I call her now. You wait.'

As well as a switchboard, Juliet saw that he operated an intercom system, and she guessed that this was for security purposes. Jan, she thought, was fortunate to be able to afford an environment where such procedures were standard.

'You go up now.' The commissionaire was gesturing vigorously at her from the cubicle. 'You take the lift.'

The lift looked old-fashioned with its wrought iron gates, but its workings were ultra-modern and they reached the floor indicated with stomach-lurching speed. Juliet stepped out on to the tiled passage and began to walk along it, the heels of her sandals clicking rhythmically as she searched for the correct number on the door.

She found it at last at the end of the passage and guessed that Jan must have one of the flats at the front of the building with the balcony that she had noticed when she arrived. She pressed the buzzer beside the door, noticing as she did so the small loudspeaker just above it. It was no surprise therefore when the speaker gave a crackle and Jan's familiar voice speaking with a hint of impatience said, 'Who's there?'

'It's Juliet.' She felt faintly bewildered. The commissionaire had presumably reported that she was on her way up. Who else could it be, for heaven's sake?

'Oh, Julie!' Her sister's voice sounded almost relieved. There was a rattle as a chain was unfastened inside and then the door swung open. Jan stood in the doorway smiling at her. 'Darling, what a lovely surprise!'

'Weren't you expecting me?' Juliet walked past her into the apartment and put her case down.

Jan shrugged. 'Mim mentioned something in one of her letters, but frankly I wondered if you'd go through with it. But it's marvellous to see you now you are here. How long are you staying?'

'A week, if that's all right.' Juliet found her eyes straying round the room in which they were standing. It was a large room, and built on two levels. They were standing on the upper level, a kind of gallery surmounted by a wrought iron balustrade which led presumably to the bedroom as well. Two wide steps descended into the living room, which judging by its size ran the whole length of the apartment. At one side, wide glass doors led to the balcony. Thick cream and gold carpet stretched from wall to wall, and Juliet noticed a wide chesterfield sofa upholstered in warm golden brown hide with two matching armchairs arranged with their backs to the window, and facing a wall where an elegant fitment contained a complicated-looking hi-fi unit and a television set. At the other end of the room, she saw a white baby grand piano surmounted by an alabaster vase containing long-stemmed yellow roses.

'Oh, that's fine.' Jan sounded amused. 'That's plenty of time to prepare a report for Mim. I assume that's why you're here.'

Juliet felt the colour steal into her cheeks, and her sister's smile widened.

'Don't look so stricken,' she advised. 'Mim's very transparent, you know, and you're not much better. And I don't mind—really. I suppose I could have suggested it myself, but I've been so busy.' She shrugged eloquently. 'Anyway, we'll put your case in the bedroom, and then I'll make some iced coffee. We'll have it on the balcony.'

The bedroom was also a large room, its single beds fitted with quilted gold bedspreads. There were wild silk curtains at the windows, and an entire wall was taken up with fitted wardrobes in white and gold. The bathroom which led off the bedroom was even more breathtaking, with a sunken bath and gold-plated taps shaped like dolphin's heads.

Juliet shook her head helplessly as she gazed around her. Nothing could have been further from the rambling Victorian semi-detached house where they had been born and brought up, yet Jan seemed completely at home in her exotic surroundings. It brought home to Juliet as little else could have done just how much she and her sister had grown apart. She felt alien and out of place in all this luxury.

'Do you like the apartment?' Jan sat down on the padded stool by the dressing table and gave her an amused glance.

'It's unbelievable!' Juliet picked her words with care. 'But where is Maria? I thought you were sharing with her.'

'Oh, that didn't work out,' Jan admitted casually. 'But this place is only temporary, I may say. I'm not a million-airess yet. There was a cancellation over a lease and I was able to step in on a short-term basis, at a reduced rent. I'll have to move in the autumn when they find another permanent tenant, of course, but until then it's quite pleasant to live in the lap of luxury.'

She was smiling as she spoke, and her green eyes fringed by incredibly long artificially darkened lashes were fixed candidly on Juliet's face, and why Juliet should be suddenly and certainly aware that she was lying, she didn't know. But she had always since childhood had this awareness when Jan was not telling her the truth, and she felt herself frowning slightly. Then she pulled herself together. They were not children any more. Jan was grown-up now, and entitled to a life of her own, and secrets in that life. All that mattered was that Mim was kept in blissful ignorance, and all Juliet had to do was telephone her and assure her that Jan was well and happy. Any doubts and uncertainties she might privately have she would keep to herself.

'What's the matter?' Jan tilted her head back. 'You look very solemn, sister dear. Did the flight upset you? Are you tired?'

'A little, perhaps.' Juliet shook out the dress she had unpacked from her case and hung it away in one of the wardrobes. 'A shower would be nice, I think.'

'Make yourself at home.' Jan got up restlessly. 'I'll go and see about that coffee. Come back to the *salotto* when you're ready.'

Juliet was thoughtful, as she allowed the water to trickle its blissful coolness over her body. There was something definitely odd in Jan's manner. Her welcome had been warm enough, more so in fact than Juliet had expected, but there was something guarded in her attitude.

'She's obviously afraid that I'm going to start prying,' she told herself resignedly as she wrapped herself in one of the enormous fluffy bathsheets. 'I'll just have to try and make it clear to her that I'm not interested in her private life.'

She dressed, choosing a classic shirtwaister in cool green cotton, and sliding her feet into heelless sandals. She scooped her coppery hair back from her face and secured it at the nape of her neck with a scarf that matched her dress. When she had finished, she decided that she looked presentable enough, although she could not compete at Jan's level of sophistication. She grinned rather ruefully at the idea of even attempting to wear the cream silky trousers and the daringly cut black halter top that so became her sister. She left the bedroom and walked along the gallery towards the *salotto*, her feet making little sound on the thickly carpeted floor. She could hear Jan talking somewhere in a low voice and checked momentarily, thinking that other visitors might have arrived while she was having her shower, but then she told herself she was being quite ridiculous. She was also Jan's guest, after all, and she walked forward with determination. But Jan was alone in the *salotto*, speaking on the telephone. She was smoking a cigarette in quick, jerky puffs and as Juliet watched she leaned forward suddenly, crushing the stub out in a black onyx ashtray that stood by the telephone. As she did so, she glanced up and saw Juliet on the gallery. She smiled and lifted a hand in greeting, and her voice was pitched a little more loudly as she went on talking. Finally with a gay '*Ciao, caro*,' she replaced the receiver in its rest.

'I'm sorry.' Juliet came rather awkwardly down the steps into the *salotto*. 'Did I interrupt anything?'

Jan gave a smiling shrug. 'Just a phone call,' she said lightly. 'It wasn't important. Now come and soak up some of this sunshine and tell me everything that's been happening at home.'

For the remainder of the afternoon, and the evening that followed, Jan put herself out to be charming, and Juliet found herself beginning to relax and lose that sense of intrusion that had bedevilled her. They ate in the dining alcove which opened off the *salotto*—cool slices of melon, followed by *pasta* in a rich sauce.

'Your cooking has improved beyond recognition.' Juliet took an appreciative sip of the wine, and leaned back in her chair.

'I always loved Italian food. Fortunately it seems to love me too.' Jan glanced down at her slim hips with satisfaction. 'If ever I show signs of developing into a full-blown Italian *mamma*, I shall go on a permanent diet.'

'No need to worry about that,' Juliet said with affectionate admiration. 'I think you've put on a little weight, but it suits you.'

Her remark had been completely casual, and she was totally unprepared for Jan's swift glare.

'What utter nonsense!' her sister snapped. 'I'm the same weight as I've always been. Do you think, in my job, that I don't watch myself like a hawk?'

'I'm sorry.' Juliet cursed herself inwardly for tactlessness, but Jan had never used to be so touchy.

After a moment's pause, Jan smiled with an effort. 'I'm sorry too. I don't usually blow up like that, but some of the girls I work with can be such utter bitches.' She gave a rather unsteady laugh. 'I suppose I look for the knife in the back from even the most innocent remark nowadays. Thank the Lord I . . .' she broke off suddenly.

'Yes?' Juliet prompted gently.

Jan shrugged. 'Thank the Lord I can always go back to England to work if things get too bad,' she said nonchalantly, but again Juliet had the uneasy feeling that that was not the remark she had intended to make. But the next moment Jan was chatting away again, relating anecdotes about some of the famous people who went to Di Lorenzo to shop for their clothes, mimicking some of the rich women for whom she modelled, and Juliet's uneasiness passed.

As she lay in bed that night, listening to Jan's gentle breathing in the next bed, tired, but too excited to fall asleep immediately, she told herself that she was going to have a good time in Rome. Jan would be working most of the time, but she'd promised to get some time off that was owed to her to take her sister round some of the sights and perhaps do some shopping, and the evenings, she'd said, would be a different story.

While she had been clearing away the dinner dishes, Juliet had seized the opportunity to telephone her mother briefly and reassure her that everything was fine, and that she would write in more detail during the next couple of days.

She had tried to hint to Jan as they were getting ready

for bed that Mrs Laurence needed the reassurance of regular letters, but Jan had responded almost petulantly and Juliet had hastily dropped the subject.

Probably when you were miles away from home and leading a hectic working and social life, such obligations as letter-writing tended to get overlooked, she thought. And Jan was certainly in demand. The telephone had rung twice more during the evening, and although Jan had not vouchsafed any information about the callers' identities, Juliet had no doubt that they were men. There was something intimate and caressing in Jan's voice as she spoke, although Juliet could not have followed the conversation even if she had wished to do so, as her sister always spoke in Italian.

But when you were as young and as lovely as Jan, there was little wonder that men were in constant pursuit of you, Juliet thought, and it was while she was wondering a little wistfully what it must be like to be so sought after that she eventually fell asleep.

When she awoke the following morning, Jan's bed was empty, although it was still relatively early. She got out of bed and reached for the broderie anglaise dressing gown that matched her nightdress, pulling the sash securely round her slender waist before padding out on to the gallery. But as she went towards the bedroom door she heard a familiar but distressing sound coming from the bathroom. Immediately she crossed over and tapped on the door.

'Jan, love, what's wrong? Are you ill? May I come in?'

There was a pause and then Jan herself opened the door. 'Oh, hello.' Her tone was ungracious. 'There's really no need to bother. I'm fine. I must have eaten something that disagreed with me. Perhaps it was that melon—it does upset me sometimes.'

'I'll make some coffee.' Juliet gave her an anxious glance.

'Do you want to go back to bed? You look pale.'

'Of course I'm pale, I've just been throwing up. For God's sake, don't fuss. You're as bad as Mim,' Jan said impatiently.

But by the time the coffee was made and they were sitting on the balcony with fresh rolls and butter on the table, Jan had regained her colour and her good temper with it.

'Wonderful!' she exclaimed, reaching for the glass of freshly squeezed orange juice which Juliet silently extended to her. 'You are an angel. I should have invited you over long ago.'

Her eyes moved rather challengingly over Juliet's tight-lipped expression.

'Well, go on, darling. Ask me if it's true.'

'Do I really have to?' Juliet could not suppress the bitterness in her voice.

'I suppose not.' Jan finished her orange juice and set the glass down on the table. 'As a schoolmarm, I imagine you're more than capable of adding two and two together and achieving the correct result. I might have managed to keep you at bay over my weight, but I knew I couldn't hope to fool you over this foul morning sickness. I merely hoped it wouldn't happen while you were within earshot.'

Juliet met her eyes squarely. 'Were Mim and I never supposed to know?'

Jan shrugged. 'Let's just say that your visit at this precise time was—inopportune.'

'Then why on earth didn't you tell me not to come?' Juliet tried not to sound as hurt as she felt and her voice sounded flat in consequence.

'Because I was afraid that if I started putting you off with footling excuses Mim might take it into her head to come in your place. And while I might be able to fool you for a while, I knew I wouldn't escape her eagle eyes. And as you can imagine, she's the last person I want to know about this. Not until I have everything sorted out anyway.'

'What are you going to do?' Juliet asked unhappily. 'Are you going to—get rid of the baby?'

Jan's eyes opened to their widest extent. 'An abortion in Italy? You have to be joking! No, far more conventional than that. I'm getting married. In fact if you'd delayed your visit for another week or so, I probably would have been married already. All problems solved, all Mim's most romantic hopes for me gloriously fulfilled, and after a discreet interval, the promise of her first grandchild. Everything perfect.'

'I see,' Juliet said rather drily. 'That being the case, may one ask why you didn't simply get married in the first place and avoid all these rather hasty and hole-and-corner arrangements?'

Jan poured herself some coffee. 'There were reasons,' she said, frowning. 'There still are, for that matter. Mim isn't the only relative that we're keeping in the dark about our plans. Mario has a brother who's been causing us some grief.'

'In what way?' Juliet spread butter on a roll and bit into it, although she had little appetite. Jan's news had left a sick, hollow feeling in the pit of her stomach. Mim's premonition had been well founded, it seemed.

Jan shrugged again. 'Big brother feels that he should have a major say in Mario's wedding plans, and needless to say, he doesn't approve of my part in them,' she answered rather carelessly. 'Not that we've ever actually met, of course.'

'But is Mario likely to be influenced by his opinions?' Juliet could not conceal the anxiety in her tone. 'Italians are supposed to have this incredibly strong sense of family and ...'

'Well, the brother holds the purse strings for a start,' Jan broke in, spreading her hands gracefully. 'And you're right about the family feeling. They come from the South —Calabria actually, where such things matter a lot, although they don't actually live there now. Santino—that's the brother—is some kind of industrialist in the North now, and has his finger in any number of financial pies from what I can gather, including tourism.' She leaned back in her chair, lifting her face to the sun. 'I think—in fact I know—he hoped Mario would make a sensible marriage, in other words marry some other industrialist's daughter and bring about another kind of merger as an added bonus. I don't figure in his scheme of things, naturally.'

'But that's terrible,' Juliet said heatedly. 'Arranged marriages are a thing of the past, anyway.'

Jan lifted her eyebrows. 'Apparently they're still very traditional in the South. Santino's ideas aren't as extraordinary as you think.'

'But—but does he know about the baby?'

'Lord above, no!' Jan raised her eyebrows exaggeratedly. 'As a matter of fact, in view of his open hostility, we haven't told him very much at all. Mario feels it's best to maintain a low profile and just present him with a *fait accompli* after the wedding.' She sounded almost bored. 'Once we're married, there's very little he can do about it, and I doubt if he'll actually carry out any of his threats.'

'Threats?' Juliet pushed the remains of her roll away uneaten, and stared at her sister.

Jan laughed. 'Not aimed at me, silly, although I'll admit he's made some damned unpleasant remarks in the past. No, he's told Mario that he'll cut him off with the proverbial shilling—or *lira*, I suppose, to be exact. But he'll soon relent. For one thing Mario's his heir, and Santino himself isn't married or likely to be. He's far too busy making money and having a good time—the damned hypocrite! His strait-laced views on morality don't exactly extend to his own conduct,' she added on a little flash of petulance.

'I thought you didn't know him.'

'Only by repute,' Jan said. 'And I did see him once—at a safe distance in a night club. And once seen, never forgotten.'

'What is he like?' Juliet's curiosity was aroused almost in spite of herself.

'Very tall. Towered head and shoulders above everyone else around him and knew it. And as dark as Satan,' Jan said after a moment's thought. 'That's as much as I noticed, because Mario hustled me off at the speed of light out of harm's way.' She gave a faint giggle. 'Actually, I think he's a bit jealous of him. I said quite casually that I thought he was very attractive and Mario simply exploded. And he's never taken me up on any of my offers to beard the lion in his den and convince him what a simply wonderful and suitable addition I'll be to the Vallone family.'

Juliet stared at her wonderingly. Jan's tone seemed almost to be one of relish. She did not seem to care that her future brother-in-law's attitude to her was an insult. All that seemed to matter was the fact that he was an attractive man, and according to the hints she had dropped, an accomplished rake.

'I wonder why not?' she said a little grimly.

Jan smiled again rather smugly. 'As I said, I think poor Mario has always been just a teeny bit in the shade. Perhaps he was afraid that Santino might try to cut him out yet again.'

Juliet compressed her lips tightly together. 'I see,' she said with sarcasm. 'Your future relationship with your husband is obviously going to be founded on mutual trust.'

'Oh, for heaven's sake, don't be so damned suburban,' Jan said crossly. 'We don't all suffer from the same romantic illusions as you seem to. They may sing "O Perfect Love" at weddings, but that doesn't necessarily mean it exists. Mario suits me very well in a number of ways, and it's time I was thinking of getting married anyway. Modelling's fine while you're young, but people are too fond of relegating you to the scrap heap once you're over twenty. All these schoolgirls, just waiting to claw their way over you on their way up the ladder. It's almost worth the prospect of being fat and hideous for months to think that I'll be kissing all that goodbye.'

'I thought you loved it.' Juliet stared at her. 'Mim and I always thought that this was your world—your life. You could always have come home.'

'To what?' Jan demanded. 'This is all I know. I'm not trained for anything else, and I can't imagine things are any different in London from what they are here. Or do you imagine that I'll get some kind of second-rate job showing dresses in some tatty provincial department store? Thanks, but no, thanks. I'll settle for Mario instead and put up with whatever I have to from his family.' She glanced at her plain and very expensive-looking gold wristwatch. A present from Mario? Juliet found herself wondering. 'Lord, I must fly, or I'll have that Di Lorenzo bitch breathing down my neck.' She gave a slight giggle as she rose. 'I might offer to model maternity gear for her, just for the pleasure of seeing her face. 'Bye, love. See you tonight.'

Juliet's thoughts were frankly sombre as she tidied the apartment and washed the breakfast dishes. Any pleasure she might have derived from the prospect of her first day's sightseeing in Rome had been almost destroyed by Jan's news—or at least her attitude to it.

She supposed she should have been relieved for all their sakes that Jan's lover was willing to stand by her and give their child a name, and that Mim would not have to be burdened with a scandal that would wound her deeply. It was all very well to argue with herself that this was the age of the permissive society, and that unmarried mothers were no longer treated as outcasts. The world had not changed as far as Mim was concerned. If Jan had come home confessing that she was pregnant and deserted, Mim would have instantly supported and comforted her, but Juliet knew just what the cost would have been to her mother whose principles had been formed in a gentler, more old-fashioned mould. Quite apart from anything else, the fact that it was Jan, the lovely and the beloved, who had betrayed Mim's deeply held views of chaste behaviour would have been a blow from which Mrs Laurence might never have recovered no matter how brave a face she might put upon it.

Life had not been easy for her since her husband had died leaving her a widow in her late thirties. Materially they had been provided for, but Mim had never been able to hide the fact that she needed her husband's strength, and Juliet had often considered that it was a pity that her gentle, rather diffident mother had never remarried.

In their younger days, both Juliet and Jan had always taken care to protect Mim from the seamier side of life, as revealed in the media and often in the lives of those about them. There was much, they had tacitly agreed, that it was better for Mim not to know. Now Jan herself had spoiled this tender conspiracy, but what troubled Juliet was not so much the mess her sister was in but her attitude towards it and its solution.

For one thing, she had never given Juliet the slightest indication that she was in love with the unknown Mario. Juliet even had a clearer picture of the hostile and disturbing Santino than she had of her future brother-in-law. All she had really gathered about Mario was that he was in awe of Santino to a certain extent and apparently dependent on him. It was also clear that if these considerable hurdles could be cleared he was capable of giving Jan the standard of living she had apparently decided she wanted, and glancing round at the luxurious fittings of the apartment, Juliet decided wryly that this was no small consideration. But she had no idea at all how the couple actually felt about each other.

They were obviously physically attracted to each other, and presumably, if he was going to marry her in defiance of his brother's wishes, then Mario must be in love with Jan. Perhaps that was enough, Juliet thought unhappily. Hadn't someone once said cynically that in every relationship there was one who loved, and one who allowed such loving? It was not an idea that appealed to her. Juliet had no very clear idea of the man she wanted, but she had always taken it for granted that their feeling for each other would be totally mutual. Where love was concerned, half a loaf would certainly not be better than no bread at all.

On the other hand, maybe she was worrying unduly. Jan had always condemned her for being too sentimental. Perhaps now she was in love and shy about exposing her deepest feelings even to her own sister. After all, as Juliet was forced to admit, they had never been close confidantes. Jan had always had her own friends to talk and giggle with for hours on the telephone and presumably to confide in even before she left home.

Perhaps, she thought sadly, if I'd encouraged her to trust me in the past, I'd have some insight now into what she's thinking. If she doesn't love this Mario, if it's all been a terrible mistake, then it would be much better not to marry him, no matter how wealthy he may be. Even Mim would say that.

Yet at the same time she couldn't believe that Jan was marrying just for the respectability of a wedding ring. Her sister had never seemed to care much for such conventions.

She must love him, she told herself. After all, she's carrying his child.

She was torn from her reverie by the sound of the front door buzzer. Rather hesitantly, she walked over to the intercom and pressed the switch.

'Hello,' she said, feeling inadequate.

'*Scusi, signorina.*' The answering voice was male and a little startled. 'I bring flowers. You open, please.'

Juliet unfastened the chain and opened the door. Sure enough it was a delivery man in a green uniform carrying a long box, filled, as she could see through the cellophane which wrapped it, with long-stemmed red roses.

The delivery man was staring at her. 'Signorina Laurence?' he asked, producing a clipboard from beneath his arm, and indicating where she was required to sign for the flowers. For a moment Juliet hesitated, wondering whether she should explain that she was not the actual recipient for whom they were intended, but another Signorina Laurence altogether, but eventually the horror of having to explain the ramifications to someone who clearly spoke only broken English convinced her that the easiest thing to do was smile and accept the flowers as if they were hers, and she hastily signed 'J. Laurence' where his finger pointed.

'*Grazie.*' He tipped his cap, gave her a look of full-blooded admiration and departed.

Juliet closed the door and stood looking at the flowers in her arms. She could see no card to indicate who had sent them, but she thought it must be Mario, and that it was odd of him to send them at a time when he knew Jan must be out working at Di Lorenzo. But at least it was the sort of gesture which gave indisputable evidence of his devotion. However, if she left them in the box, they would probably be dead by the time Jan got home this evening.

She hunted round in the kitchen cupboards until she found a suitable jar and arranged the roses in it before carrying it through to the *salotto*. There was a small occasional table positioned by the window and she lifted it across to stand behind the sofa, and placed the vase on it where it could be seen as soon as anyone entered. It would be a nice welcome for Jan when she returned, she thought.

On her way out, she paused at the front door to make sure the key Jan had given her the previous evening was safely tucked away in an inside pocket of her shoulder bag, and to take one last look at the apartment and make sure she had left everything secure.

As she turned away, the red roses in their flamboyant beauty caught her eye. The traditional symbol of love, she found herself thinking as the lift carried her swiftly downwards, and that being so, why the sight of them should have sent an involuntary shiver down her spine, she had not the slightest idea.

CHAPTER TWO

By the time she was ready to return to the apartment, late in the afternoon, Juliet had forgotten her earlier unease in the sheer joy of finding herself in Rome for the first time.

She'd had no difficulty in deciding what to see first. She knew that Jan would draw the line at ecclesiastical architecture, no matter how renowned, so her first day's sightseeing was spent touring St Peter's.

Accordingly she found herself walking slowly up the Via della Conciliazione and into the huge Piazza which Bernini had designed centuries before. This was the scene she had glimpsed so many times on television at Easter and other festivals, and today the square seemed almost deserted in contrast, with the knots of tourists concentrating their ever-busy cameras on the famous colonnades and their statuary.

For a moment she felt almost disappointed because it all seemed so familiar, and then she saw someone going up the steps in front of her towards the church itself, and its sheer immensity took her by the throat.

She spent the rest of the day touring the church itself, exploring St Peter's from the dizzying view over Rome from the tiny balcony high up in the dome, to the early Christian grottoes. She wandered around the Treasury, gazing in awe at some of the priceless treasures which had been presented to the Vatican over the centuries, her imagination constantly stirred by them, in particular by the cloak that legend said the Emperor Charlemagne had worn at his coronation. Later, as she stood before Michelangelo's exquisite Pietà, shielded now from possible vandalism behind a glass screen, she felt involuntary tears welling up in her eyes. No photograph or other reproduction could do it justice, she realised.

She was physically and mentally exhausted by the time she had seen everything she wanted to see, and it was a relief to find a taxi and make her way back to the apartment, her mind still reeling from the overwhelming size and magnificence of the church.

As she went into the foyer of the apartment block, she looked towards the porter's cubicle to smile at the man who had wished her a cheerful happy day as she left that morning, but it was a strange face looking back rather sourly at her through the glass partition, and she guessed that the shift must have changed. She felt rather foolish as she rode up in the lift. You simply did not go round in Italy beaming at strange men, she reminded herself sternly as the lift halted and the door opened.

Glancing at her watch, she supposed it would still be some time before Jan returned, although she had little idea of the sort of hours her sister worked. Sure enough, the apartment was empty as she let herself in, and yet she had the immediate feeling that it was not quite as she had left it.

Again, she found her eyes travelling to the vase of red

roses, and her heart gave a small painful thump as she saw a large white envelope leaning against it. Cool it, she told herself. You're getting as bad as Mim with her premonitions.

The envelope was addressed to her and it was Jan's writing. She could not repress a feeling of alarm as she tore it open, and the contents were hardly reassuring.

'Darling,' wrote Jan, 'Sorry to leave you in the lurch like this, but I must go away for a few days. Big brother is out to make trouble, and I simply can't risk waiting any longer. Next time I see you, I shall be Signora Vallone. Wish me luck. Yours. J.'

Juliet stared down at the note, her heart pounding, then a sudden feeling of anger overwhelmed her and she tore the paper into tiny pieces. Her own sister was getting married, and these few curt lines of explanation were all the announcement or involvement that she could hope for. And for Mim, of course, it would be even worse.

It had apparently not occurred to Jan that her sister might wish to witness the ceremony, even if she was dispensing with such luxuries as bridesmaids. She had not even permitted her to meet the bridegroom before the wedding took place.

She went through to the kitchen and disposed of the torn fragments and the envelope in the refuse bin, telling herself to calm down. There was little point in wishing that Jan was other than she was. She had always been very lovely and very selfish, and the spoiling that her loveliness had induced had merely increased the selfishness, she thought rather desolately.

She looked round her irresolutely. There was plenty of food, she knew. All she had to do was prepare some. And things could be very much worse, she reminded herself. True, she was disappointed that Jan was getting married in haste and secrecy, but judging by the reference to Santino Vallone in her note, she had her reasons. But she had the free run of the apartment in Jan's absence, and only herself to consider for the next few days.

But she did not feel like a lonely meal after her solitary day. Jan would probably not have been particularly interested to hear about her experiences, but she would have lent an indifferent ear all the same. Now there was no one to share even at the remotest level her sense of wonder at all she had seen, or listen to her plans for the following day, and she felt almost childishly hurt.

Oh, damnation, she thought angrily, brushing the stinging tears from her eyes with a dismissive hand. She was in grave danger of relapsing into self-pity, which was not a failing she usually suffered from. What she had to do now was make the most of her remaining time in Rome, because when Jan returned she would be on her honeymoon, and that was a situation which she would not be able to intrude upon no matter how lonely she might feel. Jan's return in fact would have to be the signal for her departure.

But she wouldn't spend the evening brooding. She would shower and change and go out for a meal. The decision made, she felt infinitely more cheerful. As her stay was going to be inevitably curtailed, she could afford to splurge a little bit more on her daily spending. She walked through the bedroom and into the bathroom beyond, discarding sandals and clothes as she went.

It was bliss to wash the dust and heat of the day from her body under the shower, and she didn't bother to use the shower cap hanging on the peg by the tiled cubicle. There was a range of talcs and toilet waters on a glass shelf above the bath and she sampled a few of them before scenting herself liberally from the most exotic. She picked up a towel and rubbed at her damp hair which tumbled in a copper cascade about her naked shoulders. She was just on the point of returning to the bedroom when she heard the door buzzer sound.

There was a towelling robe hanging on the back of the

door and without pausing she grabbed at it, thrusting her
arms into the sleeves and tying the belt round her slim
waist. At the top of her mind was that it could be Jan, or
even Mario come to invite her to go with them to what was,
after all, a family occasion. As she hurried barefoot along
the gallery towards the door, it occurred to her that the
robe was much too large for her. In fact it would also have
been much too large for Jan as well, and flushing slightly
she realised it must belong to Mario. Perhaps he had merely
moved out for a few nights to accommodate her, she
thought as she fumbled for the chain on the door. In any
case, it was none of her business.

The buzzer sounded again, loud and imperative, and in
her haste she forgot all about the preliminary precaution
of using the door intercom. Even as the door swung open,
a warning note sounded inside her head, but by then it was
too late, because the man who had been waiting impatiently
on the threshold was already pushing his way past her into
the apartment.

Juliet controlled a gasp of fury. Who does he think he
is? she raged inwardly as the newcomer strode down the
steps to the *salotto* and stood looking around him. If it was
Mario, brother-in-law or no, she would give him a piece of
her mind, but suddenly it was borne in upon her that Mario
would surely be a younger man, and an unpleasing conviction began to take hold of her mind as she studied her
peremptory visitor.

She felt at an utter disadvantage, of course—her hair
hanging round her face in damp tendrils, and wearing nothing except this robe which plainly didn't belong to her.
She was in no fit state to cope with anyone—least of all
this stranger who behaved as if he owned the place.

He was very dark, she saw, with thick hair untouched
with grey, growing back from his forehead. He was deeply
tanned with a high-bridged nose and a mouth that despite

its sensual curve looked as if it had never uttered the word 'compromise' in its life. His eyes, when he swung back to look at her, were surprisingly light in colour—almost tawny, she found herself thinking, and oddly sinister against the darkness of his skin. And he was good and angry. About that there wasn't the slightest doubt.

For reasons she could not have explained even to herself, Juliet found that she was instinctively tightening the sash of that stupid robe.

He rapped a question at her in Italian, and she shook her head.

'I'm sorry.' She was ashamed to hear a slight tremor in her voice. '*Sono inglese. No comprende.* Do you speak English?'

'Of course I speak English,' he snapped furiously, and so he did, faultlessly with barely a trace of an accent. 'But I understood, *signorina*, that you spoke fluent Italian. Or is that merely another of the fairy stories that my impressionable brother has chosen to believe about you?'

Juliet swallowed. So her instinct had been right. His height alone should have warned her. He was certainly taller than most of the men she had seen that day, lean too, in an expensive dark suit with a silky texture. He had pushed the jacket back and was standing watching her, his hands resting lightly on his hips. But there was no relaxation in his pose. She was reminded all too strongly of a mountain lion about to spring.

What had Jan said? As dark as Satan, and she was right, except for those curious tawny eyes. But perhaps she hadn't been close enough to him to notice them, Juliet thought, and wished very much that she wasn't either, particularly when they appeared to be contemptuously stripping her naked.

Trying to steady her voice, she said, 'I think, *signore*, that you have made a mistake.'

He smiled grimly. 'On the contrary, *signorina*, it is you that has made the mistake. I ordered you to leave my brother alone. I offered what I believe were generous terms for you to do so, yet you have ignored my letter and flagrantly disobeyed my orders.'

Juliet's lips parted soundlessly. Jan had said she had only seen him once and that at a distance, but had he seen her? It seemed not, or he would never have mistaken her for her sister.

A feeling of helplessness was beginning to overwhelm her. She simply wasn't prepared for this. Jan had mentioned no letter nor any offer of terms, only talked vaguely of threats. Stealing a glance at Santino Vallone, Juliet could well believe that he would carry out any threat that he might utter. The dark face wore an expression of almost patrician disgust as he stared at her, but there was a ruthlessness about its hard lines that it was impossible to ignore. Formidable was a word she rarely used, but it applied to him.

The thought came to her that Jan might have been expecting this visit and might have deliberately absented herself, but she crushed it under. Jan had gone away to get married, and this man was here to put a spoke in the wheel of her wedding plans if he could. Only—he thought she was Jan, and clearly he had no idea that her marriage to his brother was so imminent.

All she had to do was explain, show him her passport from her handbag in the bedroom and he would leave. But he would leave in search of Jan and Mario and it was possible, even probable, that he would find them and perhaps even prevent the wedding taking place. Jan was obviously more disturbed by his influence than she had revealed, or why her hurried and secretive departure?

But if—if she let him go on believing that she was Jan, it was just possible that she could keep him on a string for a few days until the wedding was over and his interference no longer mattered. At the very least, she could give Jan and Mario a head start.

She flung her head back and lifted her chin. Her eyes sparked back at him. 'Orders, *signore*? Who gave you the right to give me orders?'

He made an impatient gesture. 'We are not here to talk of rights, *signorina*,' he said coldly. 'I have come to offer you for the last time the terms I stated in my letter. I understood from your reply that you were willing to consider them, but I am not prepared to put up with any more prevarication from you.'

Juliet digested his words in silence, her brain whirling feverishly. She seemed to be getting into deep water already. What could he mean? Had Jan actually written to him, and if so had she merely been pretending to agree to his terms in order to win time? Surely that was the answer. She could never have seriously considered his offer to buy her off. Juliet wouldn't believe it. Jan could never have permitted such a consideration to enter her mind, she argued with herself vehemently. Her sister must simply have been playing for time.

She gave a little shrug. 'You're clearly so used to having people accede to your slightest wish, *signore*, I was afraid what the shock might do to you if I said what I really thought.'

The tawny eyes swept over her and she was aware of a daunting blaze in their depths.

'Indeed, *signorina*?' he drawled. 'I think my system can stand the strain. What was wrong with the offer? Didn't it contain sufficient money?'

A cold fury possessed Juliet. Whatever faults Jan might have, she was her sister, and no arrogant Italian male, however wealthy, was going to insinuate that she was some kind of cheap gold-digger eager to be bought off for some unknown amount of cash.

Her tone was dulcet, but her smile was dangerous as she

said, 'You don't have sufficient money, *signore*. It's Mario that I want, and no amount of bribery by you can alter that, so please don't try.'

His lip curled. 'I admire the note of conviction, *signorina*, but I don't believe it. I also have my convictions, and one of them is that most men have their price, and all women. I am merely waiting to hear yours.'

She longed to do something thoroughly unladylike, like slapping him hard or raking her fingernails down his smooth tanned cheek, but she had to forget her own angry impulses and play the scene as if she were Jan.

Jan wouldn't allow herself to be thrown by her déshabille and damp hair. She would have smiled, pouting a little at his discourtesy, and pushed back her hair, letting the robe open slightly at the front so that Santino Vallone was aware that under it she wore nothing but her perfume. She would have enticed him to a more approachable frame of mind, and played him like a fish on a hook with her audacious beauty.

But knowing what Jan would probably have done and acting on it herself were two entirely different things. And the depressing part of it was that Juliet didn't have a clue where to start. Men like the arrogant Santino Vallone were totally out of her league. Yet she had to try if she was to continue to convince him that she was Jan.

'Lost for words, *signorina*?' came the jibing remark. 'Or are you too busy doing sums in your head?'

She made herself smile at him. 'Actually, *signore*, I was just thinking I find your low opinion of women in general and myself in particular rather distressing.' She strove for lightness of tone. 'I'm wondering what I can do to redress the balance.'

His brows rose sardonically. 'So the little bird has decided to sing a different tune. Bravo! And yet you are very charming when you're angry, *cara*, or at least when you're pretending to be. No wonder you've had such a devastating effect on my gullible brother. But that little game's over now—or was when you decided to break the rules, so let's not waste any more time.'

'I'm sorry,' Juliet shrugged, and felt the towelling robe slip away from one shoulder. Her immediate instinct was to drag it back into place and it took all the self-command of which she was capable to leave the revealing folds of fabric where they were. She could feel his eyes on her, frankly assessing, lingering over the exposed line of her throat and the creamy skin of her bare shoulder, and she could feel a tight knot of fear in her chest—fear and something perilously approaching excitement. Her hands began to ball into fists at her sides and she made herself relax. Jan, she thought wryly, would never tie herself into a mass of tensions just because a man was looking at her. Besides, she was supposed to be a successful model who was used to being looked at. And to be fair to herself, she wouldn't be fighting this strange sort of panic under normal circumstances. Only these were not really normal circumstances, and this was not just any man.

She rallied herself defensively. 'But I don't quite understand you, *signore*. What game are you referring to and what rules am I supposed to have broken?'

'Quite the guileless innocent, aren't you, *cara*, when it suits you to be. The game is love, for want of a better word, and the rule is that a woman like you does not expect the man to marry her.'

She had half expected what he was going to say, but the shock of hearing it brutally spelled out was sickening. She felt as if a fist had been driven into the pit of her stomach, and her breathing quickened perceptibly.

His words did not apply to her—she knew that, and that should have lessened their impact, yet that was impossible because they applied to Jan instead. How dared he? she thought as hurt and bewilderment fought with the anger inside her. How dared he say such things—make such insinuations about Jan?

Clearly he must know that she and Mario had been living together, at least on a casual basis, and this was the reason for his condemnation. That was the traditional viewpoint after all. The man could be as wild as he chose, but the girl must be pure, jealously guarding her virginity for her wedding day. And because Jan had transgressed this unwritten law with her future husband, she was regarded as an outcast. The colour rose faintly in her cheeks as she realised that Santino had probably recognised the bathrobe that she was wearing at that moment as Mario's and drawn his own conclusions.

She remembered too Jan's bitter remarks about his hypocrisy. It was the ultimate in male chauvinism, she thought angrily, to use women for his own cynical pleasure and then despise the woman who had been his partner in that pleasure. Besides, Jan and Mario loved each other. Didn't that enter into the reckoning? She found her own resolution hardening. She and Santino Vallone would play a whole new game, and this time she would invent the rules.

She smiled at him, her long lashes brushing her cheeks. 'Your argument should be with Mario, *signore*. After all, it was he who proposed marriage to me, not the other way round.'

'But I only have your word for that, *cara*,' he said softly, with a sting underlying every word.

She pretended to wince, laughing a little as she did so, controlling her own rage and contempt. 'Ouch, you play dirty, *signore*, and that's not in the rules either.'

'I write my own,' he said quite pleasantly, and she believed him. Quite inconsequentially she found herself wondering how he would react when he discovered the truth about her deception, but she comforted herself with the reflection that by the time that happened she would be safely back in England and Jan and Mario would have to bear the brunt of his wrath together. Besides, she reasoned, Jan could always say with perfect truth that she'd had no idea what her sister had been up to in her absence.

'You seem nervous,' he observed.

'Is it any wonder?' She moistened her lips with the tip of her tongue. She had not intended it to be provocative—her lips were genuinely dry—but she saw his slight reaction to it and her confidence grew. 'You—you disturb me.'

'I'm flattered, *cara*.' He sounded amused. 'And you, I need hardly say, would disturb any red-blooded male.'

'Do you include yourself in that category?' she asked impudently.

'Need you ask?' He was drawling again.

She shrugged. 'I'm intrigued, that's all. I understood that it was because blue blood flows exclusively in the veins of the Vallone family that my candidature was unwelcome.'

She'd drawn a bow at a venture, but she knew she'd hit the target. She sent him a demure glance and saw that he was laughing openly.

'Poor Mario,' he said. 'He never stood a chance, did he? And where is he? Skulking in the bedroom perhaps, afraid to show himself?'

'Oh, no.' She was startled by the unexpectedness of the question and came close to faltering. Naturally he would expect her to know Mario's whereabouts, but could she manage to stall him on that as well? 'I—I haven't seen him today.'

He was no longer laughing, his brows drawn together in a dark frown.

'That is curious. I missed him at the office and was told that he was meeting you here.'

'Well,' she shrugged, 'perhaps he changed his mind.' She walked away and began to fiddle aimlessly with the roses. 'Perhaps he's changed his mind about everything and you don't have to worry anymore. Have you considered that, *signore*?'

'I doubt it,' he said drily. 'For one thing, you don't find the prospect nearly worrying enough, *cara*. No woman sees a potential meal-ticket vanishing without making at least some effort to recover it. If you had any fears of Mario's deserting you, then you'd have come to terms with me long ago.'

She pretended to yawn. 'Well, the meal-ticket is elsewhere just now, *signore*. Which is a pity really, because it's past time for dinner, and I'm starving—so if you'd excuse me . . .'

He consulted his watch. It was platinum, she noticed, and so were the elegant links in the cuffs of his silk shirt.

'Go and pretty yourself, *cara*,' he said almost brusquely. 'I'll take you to dinner.'

Juliet was frankly taken aback. She hadn't intended him to react like that. The strain of this play-acting was beginning to tell on her, and she had hoped he would take the hint and leave.

'But you don't want to dine with me,' she said uncertainly. It was Juliet speaking now, all the assumed bravado dropping from her like a cloak.

'I didn't, it's true, but I find it an idea that gains in appeal with each minute that passes.' His lips curled in apparent self-derision. 'Hurry and dress, *bella mia*, while I phone and book a table for us.'

She was about to protest again, but she hesitated. He was going to find it acutely suspicious, if, having led him on as she had to admit she had been doing, she now displayed a genuine reluctance to be in his company.

She groaned inwardly. She was hungry all right. She'd

made do with a simple lunch of fruit, but the thought of another couple of hours in his company, this time in the secluded intimacy of a restaurant, was calculated to destroy her appetite. Jan would have carried the whole thing off without a tremor—she'd wanted after all to beard the lion in his den, but she—all she wanted was some peace. She had no real confidence that she would be able to continue with her self-imposed charade over the next few days. If she had to, she would leave the flat and trust to luck that she would find a cheap hotel somewhere, and that Santino Vallone wasn't having her watched, a course of action she was certain would not be beyond him.

She gave him a cautious glance beneath her lashes. That terrifying anger she had glimpsed seemed to have subsided for the moment, but she sensed that it was still there just beneath the surface and she had no wish to unleash it again.

She managed a breathless little laugh. 'Well, thank you, *signore*. But I wonder what the gossip columnists will make of you dining *tête-à-tête* with your future sister-in-law?'

He had the telephone receiver in his hand and was in the act of dialling, but he turned slightly and looked at her over his shoulder.

'I imagine they'll draw the appropriate conclusions,' he said softly. 'And allow me to remind you yet again, Janina *mia*, that you have no future as my sister-in-law.'

He turned his attention back to his telephone call and Juliet fled.

Once in the bedroom, she gave a swift glance along the brief line of clothes hanging in her section of the wardrobes, and shook her head. They were all strictly Juliet dresses, and none of them appropriate for the role she was playing. She gave a longing glance at one new dress she had brought for this holiday—white with bands of delicate Swiss embroidery, cut in an Empire style which showed off her slenderness and gave her an air of fragility.

But for an evening in a smart Rome restaurant with Santino Vallone, fragility was the last effect she wanted to achieve. She pushed the sliding door along and stared at the racks of clothes belonging to Jan. There was bound to be something here that she could use. She wondered where Santino was taking her, and hoped fervently that it would not be a restaurant where Jan was known. She couldn't hope to keep the deception going with someone who would recognise Jan on sight, although she supposed there was enough of a superficial resemblance to pass at a distance. They were about the same height and build and their colouring was similar, and she supposed this was why Santino Vallone had not questioned her identity. He had expected to meet a red-haired English girl at the apartment, and his expectations had been fulfilled, although not quite in the way he thought.

She seized a dress at random and held it against herself, looking at her reflection in the full-length mirror. It was black and ankle-length, the skirt of a silky crêpe, and the long-sleeved bodice in exquisite black lace. It was far more *décolletée* than anything she had ever worn, but she just had to hope it would give her the air of sophistication that she needed.

Her hair was another problem. Although it was almost dry again, it would not be appropriate to tie it back in her usual simple style, and she supposed the most sensible thing to do would be to twist it into a smooth knot at the nape of her neck. Nor could she hope to imitate Jan's expertise with cosmetics, just make sparing use of eyeshadow to accentuate the green in her eyes, and relieve some of the pallor in her cheeks with blusher. She was not dissatisfied with the result when she had finished, and her hairstyle was very becoming, she thought, showing off her small ears and the delicate line of her jaw. No matter how tremulous she might feel, outwardly she looked poised and in control of the situation, and that was as much as she could hope for. She gave herself one last look and turned to reach for her dress which she had left lying across the bed.

From the doorway, Santino said coolly, 'Charming. My respect for Mario's judgment, if not for his common sense, increases by leaps and bounds.'

Juliet couldn't suppress the startled cry that rose to her lips. All she was aware of were his eyes appraising her, as she stood there defenceless in the lacy black waist slip, and the half-cup bra which lifted her rounded breasts without covering them. Her face flamed and she snatched up the dress, holding it in front of her.

'How dare you walk in without knocking!'

His brows rose. 'Why the pretence at modesty, *cara*? You've worn more revealing garments every day, I'm certain, on that catwalk at Di Lorenzo with more eyes upon you than mine, not to mention that more private performance that I was privileged to glimpse at the Contessa Leontana's party a few months ago.'

She was too embarrassed to heed his words closely. She knew that Jan would have outstared him, and it was true that girls wore less than she had on now every day on the beaches of the Mediterranean and the Adriatic, and if she herself had been sunbathing in a bikini she could probably have borne his scrutiny. But this was not a beach, it was a bedroom, and she'd never been in this kind of situation half-clothed with a man before. It might be utterly ridiculous in this day and age, but it was true. In some ways she was as old-fashioned as Mim herself.

She said with as much ice as she could manage, 'I prefer to keep my private and my professional lives strictly apart, if you don't mind, *signore*. Perhaps you'd be good enough to return to the *salotto* and wait for me there.'

He stared at her for a moment, frowning a little as if she had bewildered him, then he gave a low laugh and turned away.

'Well, hurry then,' he tossed at her. 'You surely don't take this long to change at Di Lorenzo?'

Her hands were shaking so much she could hardly adjust the zip of the dress, but at last she was ready. She bit her lip as she saw for the first time just how revealing the bodice really was, but she told herself that it was too late to change again, and anyway it was exactly the sort of dress that Jan would have worn. She snatched up the black velvet purse she had found wrapped in tissue on one of the wardrobe shelves and went towards the door.

Santino Vallone was sitting on one of the sofas glancing through a magazine as she came along the gallery, and for a moment she was afraid. Suppose it was one of the magazines that used Jan for their fashion spreads? From what she knew of her sister, she would be quite narcissistic enough to have them lying round the apartment. She hesitated slightly as she reached the top of the steps, wondering whether he would jump to his feet, his face grim and accusing, and what she would be able to salvage from the wreck if he did, but he merely laid the magazine aside and got to his feet. He stood looking at her for a long moment, and there was an odd expression deep in the tawny eyes. Then he strolled forward, pausing to break off one of the deep crimson roses as he came.

He walked slowly up the steps, his eyes effortlessly holding hers. She found herself thinking desperately that it was as if she had been mesmerised. She could not look away, and she felt that betraying blush rising again. He reached her side and before she could guess his intention, he leaned forward and slipped the rose into the revealing vee of the deeply slashed lace bodice, between the shadowy cleft of her breasts, and for one heart-stopping moment she felt his fingers brush against her flesh.

Then he stood back critically to view his handiwork, a faint smile lifting the corners of his mouth.

'An enchanting contrast in textures,' he remarked with a coolness she was not capable of emulating. 'The velvet of the rose against the silk of your skin. You are worth waiting for, Janina *mia*.'

And while she was still breathlessly taking in what he had said, including his last enigmatic remark, he put his hand under her arm, and led her to the door.

CHAPTER THREE

HE was an expert driver, but then naturally he would be, Juliet thought crossly as the low-slung sports car purred its way almost noiselessly through the evening traffic.

She wanted to ask where they were going, but felt it was better to pretend that she knew, and she tried not to look too eagerly around her as they drove through part of the city she had never seen before. Jan, she was sure, would take her surroundings very much for granted.

Her companion seemed silent as they drove and she was thankful for it. All sorts of snags which she had not previously taken into consideration were now beginning to occur to her—the major one being that she would probably be expected to be quite conversant with any number of intimate details about Mario and his immediate family, not to mention his friends. What on earth was she going to say if Santino began to question her on the subject? She would be bound to make all sorts of glaring errors, and his suspicions would be aroused at once. He was no doubt already thinking that it was odd that a girl who worked in

Rome should have next to no knowledge of the Italian language, unless he had simply concluded that she was too lazy to learn it.

Juliet found herself wishing that she had made her identity known at the very start, and steadfastly denied all knowledge of Mario and his involvement with her sister. She could have pretended that Jan had sub-let the apartment to her—all kinds of explanations and excuses, some more convincing than others, were coming to mind. Anything, she thought ruefully, would probably have been better than the web of deceit she had started to spin. It would only take a little judicious probing from the brooding man beside her, and her whole fragile fabrication would come tumbling down.

She hoped apprehensively that the restaurant would not be too fashionable. The fewer people she was seen by the better. And the darker the restaurant was the better too, she told herself. By candlelight, in a secluded corner, she might just be able to pass for Jan if she was seen at a distance by someone who actually knew her sister.

But her hopes were dashed when they finally reached their destination. Santino had chosen a restaurant right on the outskirts of the city. It was large, popular and quite clearly expensive, and their table, far from being hidden in some dark corner, was almost in the centre of an enormous terrace, overlooking exquisite formal gardens, and with a panoramic view of the city itself.

Juliet found herself the cynosure of all eyes as she walked to the table, and she had not been in Rome long enough to be untroubled by the frankness of some of the masculine glances and *sotto voce* remarks which pursued her. She sank rather thankfully into the chair the waiter was holding for her, and hoped she had managed to mask her embarrassment at the small ordeal. It was the kind of situation that Jan would have revelled in, she supposed, being escorted by someone as dark and devastating as Santino Vallone. It was quite a relief to shelter from prying glances behind the huge menu that she was handed. She wondered with dismay if she was supposed to appear knowledgeable about the choice of food being offered, and heard her companion give a low-voiced order to the waiter for two dry Martinis to be brought to them.

He leaned back in his chair and gave her an enquiring look. 'What do you wish to eat, Janina? A simple steak and a salad, perhaps?'

'Certainly not,' she denied indignantly, her eye focussing on a magnificent trolley laden with *hors d'oeuvres* which a waiter was steering between the tables.

He raised his eyebrows slightly. 'You do not fret perpetually about your weight? *Meraviglioso!*'

Juliet suddenly found herself thinking of the idle remark she had made to Jan—a lifetime ago, it seemed. Could it really be only twenty-four hours? She flushed a little.

'No,' she said with constraint, 'not at the moment.' She glanced about her, casting round for a change of subject, wanting to get away from any personal element. 'What a magnificent view!'

'Have you never been here before?'

She lifted one shoulder casually. 'I don't think so. I don't remember ...'

'One goes to so many places,' he finished for her, rather mockingly. 'You are a true Roman, Janina. I am surprised that you still find the skyline romantic.'

'I didn't say that,' she said stiffly.

'No,' he agreed. 'You said "magnificent", but I saw a dream in your eyes.'

She looked down embarrassed at the polished wood of the table in front of them. It seemed she would have to guard her eyes now, as well as her tongue.

He went on rather drily, 'I see what you see, and yet my

vision is filled with roofs and towers and domes. They do not belong to my own concept of magnificence.'

'Which is?' The drinks arrived, and it was in some ways a relief to have the coolness of the glass in her hand and be able to run her fingers down the slender stem.

He shrugged. 'Many things, but none of them to do with cities. Perhaps—a fortress, half in ruins on the edge of a cliff, looking across a violet sea to an island all greens and amethyst in the evening light.'

'A particular place?'

'A particular place,' he agreed. He lifted his glance. 'To what shall we drink?'

Juliet was emboldened by this sudden unexpected glimpse behind the mask of worldly arrogance. 'To our better understanding?' she suggested shyly.

'I think not.' His voice was cool and edged again. 'I understand you quite well enough as it is, *cara*.'

She felt quite absurdly hurt, although what more had she expected, for heaven's sake? She lifted her glass in turn. 'Very well, *signore*. To—absent friends.'

'You said that with a certain relish, *mia*.' He was watching her through half-closed eyes. 'I presume, however, that you refer to Mario. Perhaps it is as well that he is absent. What would he say, do you suppose, if he knew we were here together?'

She sipped her drink and set the glass down before answering. 'This is hardly a private rendezvous,' she said. 'He wouldn't object.'

'You imagine not?' He smiled unpleasantly. 'You seem to forget that Mario is from the South as I am. We may pay lip service to present-day manners and morals, but it is a veneer, nothing more. In our hearts is an older, more savage tradition, as you may find out to your cost, *cara*. We Southern men can be jealous, both of our own honour and that of our women.'

'But that can't apply here and now. You're his brother,' she said.

'And that gives you some kind of immunity?' His mouth twisted. 'You deceive yourself, *mia*. But Mario would not be deceived.' He gave her a long look. 'Perhaps you should remember that.'

Jan had spoken of threats, she thought, and she had been right. His whole attitude was a threat. She had been quite mad ever to get involved with such a man. She could flounder irretrievably at any time, and it would be no good then to protest that she had meant well.

Her voice was subdued as she told him what she wanted to eat, and she sat gazing down at her clasped hands as he gave the waiter their order.

In other circumstances, it came to her, this evening could have been the culmination of her lifetime's dreams. As they had walked to the table, she had seen how the other women were watching Santino Vallone, and she would not have been human if their envy had not given her a slight sense of exhilaration. But it had brought home to her as nothing else could have done just how tepid the relationships were that she had enjoyed up to now, and this was a viewpoint that she found both disturbing and dangerous under the circumstances.

Santino Vallone might make her feel very angry, and very bitter on Jan's behalf, but she had to admit she had never felt more alive either, and it would be very hard to return her borrowed plumes and return to her normal placid routine when this strange evening was over.

One thing was certain. Even if circumstances had not decreed that they could never meet again, he was a man she had to avoid anyway for her own peace of mind. Their worlds had collided briefly, that was all. It was strange to think that even at this moment they might be related by marriage—strange and disturbing too. She wondered if

Mario was in any way like his brother, and concluded that he could not be. A younger version of Santino would not have sat down tamely under any dictatorial edicts about his marriage plans, she thought.

She had looked all round the apartment earlier but she had not been able to find a photograph of Jan's fiancé anywhere. In fact the whole place had been oddly devoid of any little personal touches as if Jan had been determined to subdue her entire personality. Perhaps Jan had considered that anything else would be a waste of time as she was only to be a temporary tenant. Another point suddenly occurred to Juliet. She had no idea where her sister and brand-new brother-in-law intended to live when they returned. Would they move into the apartment, or would they leave it vacant and move to wherever Mario was living? All Juliet hoped was that the newlyweds did not have any optimistic plans about moving in with Santino.

Then the food began to arrive and resolutely she put Jan and her problems to one side of her mind. This was her first and probably her last dinner in a top-line Roman restaurant, and she was going to enjoy every minute of it, in spite of the reckoning that her sixth sense warned her was to come.

Her plate was loaded first with tiny sardines and prawns, with glistening tomatoes and wedges of pepper, anchovies and shiny olives, and these delights were followed by lasagne, rich in creamy sauce.

She had wondered if she would have any appetite at all, but the fresh air was making her hungry, and subduing her apprehensions. A velvet twilight was beginning to descend and waiters were coming round the tables lighting the candles that were set beneath gleaming glass globes in the centre.

The main course was slices of veal simmered slowly in Marsala with tiny mushrooms, and this was accompanied by huge dishes of green beans, and tender broccoli. Juliet savoured every delectable mouthful, complemented by the smooth delicacy of the wine he had chosen.

He ate sparingly, she noticed, which probably accounted for the fact that he did not appear to have a spare ounce of flesh anywhere on his tall muscular body—something which could not be said for the majority of men at the surrounding tables, she thought frankly.

She could not face the idea of a rich dessert, and she was glad she had resisted when the waiter brought a bowl heaped with enormous peaches and cherries and lush black grapes and set it between them. There was brandy too in big balloon-shaped glasses, and coffee, strong and dark, in an elegant pot set to keep warm on a small spirit stove at one side of the table.

'And now,' Santino said very quietly. 'And now, *cara*, we talk.'

Juliet swallowed some of her brandy the wrong way and only the presence of some unsuspected guardian angel saved her from the ignominy of a coughing fit.

When she could trust her voice, she said feebly, 'There —there's nothing to talk about.'

'You think not?' He took a silver case from his pocket, extracted a long dark cheroot and lit it contemplatively. 'You are ready then to accept the terms I offered without further discussion? *Bene*.'

'No.' She shook her head quickly. 'No—your terms are totally unacceptable. I thought I had made that clear.'

'You have made nothing clear.' His voice was hard. 'What is it that you want? More money? You will be disappointed. I will not join in a private auction of my brother's future with you. The amount I have already offered is more than generous, as I think any lawyer would advise you.'

She was going to protest that she had no lawyer, but had to bite her tongue instead. It was possible, she thought,

that Jan might have taken legal advice over this man with
his threats and his bribes. Trying to maintain her part of
the conversation was rather like fencing in the dark, but it
would not be for much longer. When he saw that she was
adamant, he would take her back to the apartment, and first
thing in the morning she would find out about flights back
to England and try and get a cancellation on the first. She
would leave a note for Jan and Mario, telling them what
she had done, she thought. By that time they would be
safely married, and nothing he could do would harm them.

'Your idea of generous behaviour differs from mine,
signore,' she said in a small, cold voice, and was sorry he
would never understand the irony in her words.

His brows rose in incredulity. Then he gave a short,
sardonic laugh. 'It is hardly believable,' he said, half to
himself. 'The face and body of a Botticelli angel concealing
the soul of a cheap little gold-digger. I pity you, *mia*. You
are doomed to unhappiness, I think.'

She stared down at the tablecloth, veiling her eyes with
her lashes, unwilling to let him see her very real indignation. Jan, she supposed, would have laughed and made
some lazy retort.

She saw him glance at his watch and sensed his growing impatience.

'Come, Janina,' he said at last. 'You cannot pretend that
you did not accompany me here tonight in order to strike
a bargain. Or are you vain enough to believe that it is
sufficient for me to spend the evening admiring your
beauty? You fill the eye, certainly, *cara*, and you appeal to
the senses, but my heart you leave cold. My offer stands.
Take it or leave it.'

As if in a dream she heard him repeat the amount of
money he was offering Jan. It was in *lira*, of course, and
she was not too experienced at converting large sums back
into their English equivalent, but even her fairly hap-

hazard calculations were enough to set her brain reeling. It was like learning you had won a major prize in a premium bond draw, she thought dazedly, and it was incredible that he should offer such a sum to anyone for purely personal reasons. But as her initial amazement began to fade, a cold anger took its place. What was this money, after all, but a calculated insult to Jan?

'Well, what do you say?' His voice was incisive, cutting across her thoughts.

She made herself utter a little laugh. 'Nothing, *signore. Niente*,' she added for good measure. 'Nothing that you can say or do will make me give up Mario. You see, I love him.'

'Love?' he questioned, and she felt seared by the blaze of contempt in his eyes. 'I doubt you even know the meaning of the word. I certainly wouldn't dignify any relationship you have ever had with Mario or anyone else with such a word. Mario is a fool—but rest assured, *signorina*, I shall not allow him to suffer for the rest of his life for his folly.'

Somehow she had to maintain her self-control when every impulse was screaming at her to fling the remains of her brandy in that dark contemptuous face.

She said coolly, 'Exaggeration seems to be another Southern quality. I doubt if Mario sees our—relationship as you put it in quite that light.'

'Oh, but he will.' He spoke quite softly, but there was a note in his voice that made her shiver in spite of the balmy warmth of the evening. As if moved by strings, her hand fluttered up and touched the rose that lay like a splash of blood against the whiteness of her skin.

He watched the nervous gesture and his smile widened unpleasantly.

His voice sank almost to a whisper. 'I shall show him—demonstrate beyond all doubt the truth about you, *cara,* and he will believe it. Take the money while you can. I shall not offer it again.'

'Go to hell,' she said steadily. 'And take your money with you.'

He shook his head, and his eyes held hers. There was no visible emotion in them now, but she sensed a determination and a resolve so strong that it frightened her.

'If I go to hell, *cara*,' he said gently, 'I shall take you with me, be very sure of that.'

Her hands were shaking, but she made herself reach for the coffee pot and pour more coffee into her cup. Miraculously, she managed it without spilling any or otherwise making a fool of herself, and then something fluttered past her face and she recoiled with a little cry, setting the pot back on the little stove with a jerk.

'Oh, what was that?'

'Merely a moth,' he said impatiently. 'The candles attract them.'

She could see now that that was all it was, a large grey moth, its wings whirring helplessly as it flew again and again against the glass globe which protected the candle flame. As she watched, the moth edged perilously near to the opening at the top of the globe.

'Oh, do something,' she appealed impulsively. 'It's going to get hurt!'

He gave her a long incredulous look, then he reached forward and cupped a hand round the struggling insect.

'What now?' he demanded. 'Shall I kill it or let it go?'

'Let it go. What else?'

He rose and threaded his way through the other tables to the edge of the terrace. His hand opened, and he tossed the frightened moth away into the gathering darkness.

'Moths are foolish creatures,' he said almost meditatively as he took his seat again opposite her. 'They seem to enjoy living dangerously, yet because of this their existences are often cut short. Learn from them, *mia*. Keep away from the candle flame tonight and you too could live to play with fire again another day.'

Her head was aching suddenly with sheer tension and she had to resist an impulse to cradle it in her hands. She did not want to think too closely about the implications of what he had just said, or she might be really frightened. Just how ruthless was this man, and what power was he able to wield in his determination to achieve his own way?

'If you're trying to threaten me,' she said wearily, 'it won't work. And now I'd like to go home, please. We have nothing else to say to each other.'

She spoke bravely enough, but in reality she felt as if a million moths were fluttering with panic deep inside her. Suddenly she needed very badly to be alone for a little while to regain her composure, and she rose murmuring something idiotic about the powder room.

In the privacy of the luxuriously fitted cloakroom, she dropped on to the velvet-covered bench in front of the vanity unit and stared at herself in the mirror. The parallel he had drawn between her situation and the moth's had been an unpleasant one. She was very much aware that he made her feel that he held her too in the palm of his hand and would extend mercy or not as he chose.

'Oh, stop it,' she told herself angrily. 'You're being much too imaginative.' Like the rich food and the wine, Santino Vallone was far too heady a mixture for a suburban school-teacher from England, and she was thankful to her heart, she told herself defensively, that she would never have to see him again after tonight.

She looked again more searchingly at her reflection, and after a moment added a touch of blusher to her cheeks. What had he said about her—'the face and body of a Botticelli angel'. Natural colour rose to enhance the artificial. It was a ridiculous thing to say, she thought, an unneces-

sary and unwanted compliment. And it was untrue. Jan was
the beautiful one, and always had been. If he saw them together, he would know that. It was merely that he did not
know what Jan was like, either physically or mentally.

In a way, she felt fiercely glad that she had been there
in Rome to deal with this onslaught on her sister's behalf.
If he had got to Jan first, it would have been a sour note
on which to start her married life.

What in the world did he have against Jan anyway? He
had uttered a lot of threats and cryptic remarks, but he had
not produced one shred of tangible evidence to support his
view that she was not a suitable bride for his brother. Juliet
did not deceive herself that Jan had led the life of a recluse
since she arrived in Italy, but this was the twentieth cen-
tury after all, and Santino Vallone would have to come to
the realisation that there could no longer be one moral
law for men and another for women.

One thing was certain. Not one word of all this must
ever reach Mim's ears. She found herself wishing, for no
good reason that she could pinpoint, that Santino could
meet her mother—visit her home and see the kind of background she and Jan had come from. It might not have the
material wealth of his own family life, but surely he
couldn't be blind to all that was good in it. He would be
forced to admit that by denigrating Jan, he had been unjust
to all the Laurences.

Yet why was it important that Santino should make any
kind of admission? That was the question that began to
hum at the back of her mind and which she found herself
increasingly reluctant to answer. She'd already admitted to
herself that he was out of her league, so the kind of specula-
tion that she had been indulging in was unprofitable to say
the very least.

She glanced again at the rose, glowing against her dress,
and shivered as she recalled the brush of his fingers against

her breasts as he had placed the flower there. Even that slight physical contact with him had been like an electric current, brushing through her nerve-endings, so what would it be like to be held closely in his arms—to be kissed by him? Her face flamed hotly as she realised the exact tenor of her thoughts.

She gave a little shuddering sigh. It was utterly ridiculous to admit even to herself that she could feel a measure of attraction for someone like Santino. And such an acknowledgment, even uttered privately in her heart, was in some way disloyal to Jan. She could not respect anyone who held her own sister in such total and cynical disrespect.

She shook her head in disbelief. What in the world was happening to her? All the most important considerations seemed suddenly to have been eroded by these new and frankly overwhelming sensations that she was experiencing. She knew—or rather she had always told herself that she knew—what she wanted from a man. Could it be possible that only a few short hours spent in the company of someone totally alien to her experience could set all her ideas, all her principles madly on their respective heads?

If so, it was an unhappy prospect. Would she find herself judging each future relationship—she grimaced slightly at the word—in comparison with a man whose eyes gleamed like a mountain lion's, and whose icy tongue was quite capable of flaying the skin from your body?

And was that really all it took—that fleeting physical contact and a dinner at a candlelit restaurant—to begin this insidious bewitchment of her senses, against all reason and all logic?

No, she told herself decisively, she was not going to allow this to happen. She picked up her evening purse and rose, outwardly cool and composed, but inwardly seething with conflicting and mainly unwelcome emotions.

This mental admission of her attraction to Santino made

her departure to England even more imperative. She needed to escape quickly while she was still comparatively heart-whole. She gave a small bitter smile as she turned away. What strange and disturbing byways her impulse to impersonate Jan had led her into! She had wondered what it would be like to live her sister's life. Well, now she knew, and it had not been a comfortable experience. She would be glad to revert to being plain Juliet Laurence again, she told herself firmly.

And if she hurried back to England, she might still be in time to join that barge holiday she'd been offered. She would need something to take her mind off the past couple of days. If she simply sat at home brooding, Mim might guess that there was something wrong, and start leaping to all kinds of conclusions. Juliet shuddered at the thought of trying to evade her mother's gentle persistence once her suspicions were aroused.

But for now, she had to get through the homeward journey. The powder room door swung open at her approach and two women entered, giving her an incurious look as they swept past on a cloud of expensive scent. For a moment she lingered, wondering wildly whether she could evade Santino altogether and get a lift back to Rome from another patron of the restaurant—perhaps even these very women.

But common sense soon disabused her of that notion. How was she going to make herself understood with her limited knowledge of Italian for one thing? She could hardly go round the terrace until she found a driver who spoke sufficient English to comprehend her requirements. And did she really think Santino would stand tamely by while she stood him up—or appeared to, at least—in front of the fascinated gaze of a section of Roman high society?

No, she would have to leave with him as she had arrived, and part from him when they returned to the flat with a semblance of insouciance.

She bit her lip as she walked across the terrace to the table where he sat smoking. Why couldn't she be honest with herself, and admit that she wanted to spend just a little more time in his company, in spite of everything that he had said and the enormous gulf that must, perforce, yawn between them? The truth was that when they did part, she wanted him to think not quite as badly of her in the role she was playing as he did now, and that when the truth finally emerged, he might look back on the evening they had spent together with even a little regret.

Romantic idiocy, she told herself caustically. When he does find out what I've done, he'll probably want to break my neck.

He rose courteously at her approach, and held the chair for her to sit down again. He looked incredibly tall as he stood over her, and more formidable than ever, although he was smiling slightly.

'I have ordered fresh coffee,' he said. 'What little was left in the pot was getting stale and bitter.'

Juliet glanced down at the cup in front of her. She didn't really want any more coffee. If she drank too much of it in the evening then she didn't sleep properly. But then she didn't actually expect to get much sleep under the circumstances anyway, she thought wryly, and lifted the cup to her lips.

The fresh brew was hot, but it still had that faint bitterness Santino had mentioned, and she put the cup down after a tentative sip with a faint grimace.

'Can we go now?' she asked. 'I'm a working girl, remember? I can't take too many late nights.'

'Your looks do not seem to have suffered from them so far,' he commented, blowing a reflective smoke-ring.

She flushed and drank some more coffee to mask her embarrassment. He sat, watching her, his eyes hooded and meditative.

'I ask you one last time, Janina,' he said, and she wished,

with a sudden pang to hear her own name on his lips and not her sister's. 'Will you accept the money I have offered, go back to your own country and leave my brother in peace?'

He sounded almost tired, she thought in surprise, perhaps even a little dispirited. Maybe he wasn't used to people rejecting any offers he decided to make them, whether on a personal or a business level.

She swallowed some more of the coffee, then said quickly, 'I can't. It—it's too late. Please take my word for that.'

Later, much later, she thought, he would know what she'd meant by her hurried words.

'Your word!' he repeated, and to her dismay all the former cynicism and contempt had returned to his voice to wound her. Then he laughed shortly. 'Finish your coffee, *cara*, and we'll go. There's clearly no more to be said.'

Juliet finished the coffee and replaced the cup in its saucer. So it was all over. Waiters were bowing and smiling as they left, and she guessed that he must have settled the bill in her absence and added a generous tip.

Fate played some strange tricks, she decided as she sat beside him in the car and heard the engine purr into life. For one evening she had lived like a millionairess, only to be accused of being a gold-digger. That was an element that had been missing from all the best fairy tales, she told herself. Prince Charming had never accused Cinderella of being out for what she could get, nor had any of King Cophetua's relatives offered to buy off the beggar-maid.

It was much easier to be Juliet Laurence, schoolteacher, she thought, or would she find, when it came to it, that nothing was going to be easy for her again? That was depressive talk, she criticised herself robustly. Her pathetic charade had to come to an end sooner or later, and it was better that it was sooner rather than later when she considered some of the self-revelations that had come to her during the evening. And she wanted it to be over. There was pain and danger waiting on the path she had embarked on so recklessly. Her own life might be dull in comparison, but at least it was safe and real.

It was very warm in the car even though the side windows were open to admit the evening air. In spite of herself, she could feel an almost irresistible urge to yawn taking hold of her, and stifled it guiltily, brushing a concealing hand across her mouth. Santino Vallone, she thought, would definitely not be accustomed to women who yawned in his company.

Yet it certainly wasn't boredom she was assailed by—she felt too keyed up for that—but a sudden and inexplicable drowsiness which she found herself fighting with a strange urgency.

Santino leaned forward and flicked a switch on the dashboard and music began to play softly, with a slow sensuous beat which had an increasingly soporific effect. She forced her weighted eyelids to remain open and pulled herself into a more upright position in the seat. There was no way— no way at all in which she was going to sleep.

Now if she had been with Barry she would simply have succumbed, putting her head on his shoulder and letting her drowsiness have its way with her, but such an action would be unthinkable with a man like Santino. Even if they had merely spent a pleasant evening in each other's company with no ulterior motives on either side, she would still have been chary at putting herself so completely at his mercy.

She found another yawn threatening, and turned her head away to hide it, gazing rather desperately out of the window. Darkness outside the car, darkness within it, and the soft insistent rhythm of the music—all of it lapping her like a warm blanket, infinitely comforting, infinitely appealing. And all she had to do was let go and slide down into the darkness, closing her weary eyes and not even thinking any more because thinking, reasoning was too hard when you were so nearly falling asleep.

Through the mists that were drowning her, smothering her, she heard him say softly but with an underlying note of faint amusement, 'Why fight it, *cara*? Just close your eyes and enjoy the ride.'

It was the amusement that told her, and she grasped at it with the last remnants of reason. Her mouth felt stiff as if it didn't belong to her, and her voice seemed to come from a long way away as she heard herself say, 'The coffee —what did you put in the coffee?'

His laughter, mocking and enigmatic, was the last thing she heard as she fell asleep.

CHAPTER FOUR

SHE came awake slowly, her hand automatically reaching out to grope for the alarm clock that she felt must have triggered her subconscious. But it wasn't the usual clutter of clock, lamp, the novel she had been reading that her hand encountered. And as the sun began to filter through her still-closed eyelids, she thought, 'How stupid. Of course, I'm still in Rome at Jan's flat. But I've been dreaming about being at home.'

Then she opened her eyes and her first thought was that she was dreaming still. For the room around her bore not the slightest resemblance to the streamlined luxury at the flat. It was completely and totally unfamiliar.

She sat up, accepting that there was a slight dull ache across her forehead, her eyes questing round the room with increasing alarm. It wasn't particularly large, but it had a formidable air which was immediately apparent. Stone walls, their austerity unrelieved by any kind of hangings or colour wash, massive furniture belonging to a previous generation, small-paned windows set in deeply ledged recesses. And the bed she was lying in surely belonged more properly in a museum, she thought apprehensively as she gazed up at the brocaded canopy over her head, and the long curtains that swept down on either side of it. She supposed the curtains could be drawn round the bed at night, but last night they had not been. They had been looped back with heavily gilded and tasselled cords. The sheets and pillowcases were of linen so fine that it felt like silk against her skin, and they were edged with exquisite lace that even her untrained eyes suggested was probably handmade.

Which brought her to the next realisation—that the sheet, and the elaborately quilted and embroidered bedcover, were the only covering she had. The colour stormed into her face. Someone had brought her here, undressed her and put her to bed, and she had not the slightest recollection of any of it happening. The last thing she remembered, she forced her mind back, was music and the swift motion of a car, and a man's voice.

She pressed her hands against her burning cheeks as her memory began to stir sluggishly, and she began to recall all that had taken place—when? The previous evening? It was difficult to say, but surely she had not been to sleep for so very long?

There was a faint unpleasant taste in her mouth, and after a moment's hesitation she reached for the carafe of fruit juice which stood on the carved chest of drawers beside the bed and filled the glass, draining it to the last drop. It was deliciously cool and refreshing, and her head was beginning to clear that little bit more with each minute that passed.

She looked rather desperately round the room. Where were the clothes she had been wearing last night? she asked herself. There was no doubt in her mind that wherever she

was, Santino Vallone had brought her there, and she
writhed inwardly with shame at the thought of herself
naked and helpless under his cynical gaze.

She wanted to get out of bed and start looking in the
huge, elaborately carved wardrobe for something to wear,
but her lack of any kind of wrap made her hesitate, feeling vulnerable. After a moment she dragged at the bedcover
and twisted it around her shoulders like some exotic Re-
naissance cloak. It wasn't an ideal dressing gown by any
means, but anything was better than nothing, she thought
as she climbed out of the high bed and trod across the
thick goatskin rug which was laid over the bare wooden
floor.

The bedcover was far from being an adequate cloak. It
kept catching on things and slipping, and it was heavy, but
she held on to it tightly because it was all she had. The
literal truth of that only dawned on her a moment later
when the heavy wardrobe door swung open with a protesting squeal of hinges, and she saw that its cavernous depths
were completely empty.

She stood gazing at it with stupefaction. She hadn't expected a complete range of daywear, but at least she'd anti-
cipated that the black dress she had worn at dinner would
be there.

She swung round, hitching the bedcover up around her
shoulders, and tried the chest of drawers beside the bed.
Each drawer was carefully lined, and a bunch of some sweet
herbs was laid in each one, but that was all. And there was
no other kind of storage space in the room at all.

Juliet slammed the last drawer shut, biting her lip
angrily. Of all the ridiculous situations to be in! she
thought. She clasped the bulky folds of the coverlet more
securely round her and set off for the door. It was a solid-
looking affair with ornate hinges, and a heavy ring handle.
She twisted the ring this way and that, but it made no

difference, the door did not budge. She tugged and pulled, and in a kind of desperation even shoved at it, but all to no avail. She felt suddenly, murderously angry. She began to beat on the door with both fists, oblivious of the fact that her improvised cloak had fallen to the floor.

'Open this door!' she shouted at the top of her voice. 'Let me out, damn you! Open it, do you hear?'

The words sounded brave enough, and the noise she made was somehow reassuring, but as its echo died away, she felt suddenly forlorn, and more than a little scared. And as the minutes passed, and there wasn't the slightest response to her appeal, she began to feel cold and sick.

She turned and leaned back against the door, splaying her fingers over the sturdy timbers as if they would give her some kind of moral as well as physical support. Where was she? What was this place where she was being kept, and how long would she be forced to remain here?

Judging by the wall, it must be some kind of fortress, she thought, and remembered something Santino had said at that ill-fated dinner the previous night. Something about a fortress half in ruins and an island across an amethyst sea. Kicking the folds of the coverlet impatiently aside with her bare foot, she walked across to the window and looked out.

She seemed to be looking straight down the face of a steep cliff, and sure enough, the sea crawled there at its foot. But it was not the evening light Santino had mentioned. Judging by the position of the sun, Juliet guessed it must be around noon. Her watch had stopped at some time during the night. A shimmering heat haze hung over the water, and in the distance she could vaguely see the outline of a mass of land—possibly the island he had mentioned. She gave one last, shuddering look down and abandoned any idea she might have had of climbing out of the window. Even if she had managed to fabricate herself some kind of tunic out of one of the sheets, such a descent would have been quite beyond her.

Her shoulders slumped defeatedly as she turned away. She wanted very badly to cry, but she wouldn't allow herself the luxury. She had lost her temper already and had achieved absolutely nothing. Crying would simply be a waste of energy.

She wished she could gauge the time more accurately. She wondered how long it was since they had left the restaurant. She knew one thing—she was hungry again. She bit her lip. She had been deprived of clothes. Was Santino Vallone barbaric enough to keep food from her as well? Juliet shook her head. This was assuming the proportions of a king-sized nightmare. How long did he intend to keep her here? She would not be missed for quite some time. Jan might wonder where she had gone, but would probably assume she had drifted on to sightsee elsewhere —until she came across her clothes and her passport. Then she'd realise something was wrong. That, of course, was always assuming she returned to the apartment immediately on her return. But perhaps she wouldn't. Maybe she would simply move in with Mario and forget about the apartment —even for weeks.

Juliet swallowed. In fact the first person to sound any kind of alarm might well be Mim, and that was the last thing she wanted to happen. Wasn't it really to protect her mother and keep her in happy ignorance of the mess Jan had got herself into that she was in this predicament at all?

She groaned silently. All the tried and true maxims she had practised all her life about looking before one leapt, and the kind of tangled web that transpired when one practised to deceive, came back in force to taunt her. The whole thing was just impossible, she thought roundly. She was asleep and dreaming, and presently she would pinch herself and wake up and find that none of it had happened.

Oh, please let it be like that, she prayed inwardly, but even as the prayer took shape in her mind, she knew that it was all too true.

And just to reinforce the fact that this was cold, stark reality, she heard the sound of footsteps approaching the door.

Juliet did not wait to retrieve the abandoned bedcover, but took a flying leap into the big canopied bed, seizing the sheet and tugging it up around her neck. At the same time she was uneasily aware that the slender curves of her body were revealingly outlined under the fine linen, but it was too late to do anything about that now, because a key had grated in the lock and the door was opening.

Santino Vallone walked into the room. He was wearing denim pants and a dark close-fitting shirt, partially unbuttoned. He stood looking down at her, his hands resting lightly on his hips, and Juliet thought dazedly that this casually dishevelled beachcomber didn't bear the least resemblance to the elegantly dressed businessman she had encountered the previous evening. Except in one respect, she told herself, bitterness threatening to choke her. That incredible physical attraction she had been aware of then was there in full force, perhaps even accentuated, and she loathed herself for the undeniable response that it was evoking from her shivering body.

He looked at her lying there, not a muscle moving, the sheet tightly clenched under her chin, eyes damning him over its hem, and he smiled. The smile told her everything. It told her that he knew she was naked under its flimsy covering, and that he knew what she looked like without that covering, because he had seen her only hours before. She thought she would burn up with shame. It had been quite bad enough when he had walked into the bedroom at the apartment while she had been changing. But this—this was infinitely worse.

'Get out,' she said between her teeth.

He raised his eyebrows. 'I thought from the uproar a little while ago that you needed company.'

'Not yours,' she said, her voice shaking with rage. 'Never yours.'

He smiled again, but this time there was no amusement in it, nor even any secret knowledge. 'Then it is sad that we are condemned to each other for a while,' he said. There was a note of finality in his voice that frightened her.

After a moment, she said, 'But we don't have to be. You could just let me walk out of here. I wouldn't say anything to anyone ...' She paused. She was beginning to beg, and she must not.

But he was shaking his head slightly, the smile widening a little.

'The prospect of you walking out of here at this precise moment has its appeal,' he said drily, and her face flamed as she realised the implication in his words. 'But I regret that it is impossible.'

'But that's ridiculous!' Her breathing quickened in spite of herself and she could see his eyes on the rise and fall of her rounded breasts beneath the concealing sheet. She tried to steady herself, to remain calm and in control. Above all not to let him see that she was very near to panic, and not merely for the reasons he would expect. 'You can't keep me here against my will.'

'Nevertheless you are here,' he said coolly.

'It's kidnapping,' she protested, aware of the weakness of her words. 'That's a terribly serious offence in Italy— I know it is. You'll be caught. Someone will realise sooner or later that you're keeping me here, and then ...'

'Someone will indeed realise,' he said coolly. 'That they should is the sole reason for your being here, believe me.' He paused, his eyes holding her uncomprehending gaze, then he said softly, 'Mario.'

Even then it was several seconds before light dawned. It was as if she had almost forgotten the reckless charade she had embarked on the previous day. But he still thought she was Jan.

She said almost incredulously, 'You've gone to all this trouble simply to keep me away from Mario?' Her heart was thumping, and she kept repeating to herself like a litany, 'He doesn't know. He still doesn't realise.'

He reached for a chair, velvet-seated with an elegantly rounded back, and sat down on it astride, his arms resting negligently across the back.

He said without emotion, 'Not precisely. That, if you remember, was my original intention. When you refused the offer I made you, I had to resort to rather more drastic action. I have to ensure, you see, that Mario will wish in the future to keep away from you.' His mouth twisted sardonically. 'When he learns that you have been here with me, it will produce the desired effect. I did not exaggerate his jealous tendencies, believe me.'

She said slowly, 'But I'm not here—with you. Not like that.'

'No,' he agreed with her. 'But do you suppose Mario will believe that when he discovers your whereabouts, as I intend he shall?'

'Yes,' she improvised wildly. 'If he's your brother, he must know the lengths you're prepared to go to in achieving your own way. I'll explain to him. I'll tell him exactly everything you've said—you've done. We'll see then whom he believes.'

'We will indeed.' He smiled faintly. 'Especially as by that time, he will already have seen the newspapers.'

She stared up at him. 'Newspapers?'

He nodded. 'I'm surprised that someone as used to cameras as you are, *cara*, did not notice that we were being photographed last night at the restaurant. I also took the

precaution before we set off last night of telephoning a
journalist of my acquaintance and casually letting slip that
we were heading south together for a few weeks of sun
and pleasure.' He paused. 'He was frankly envious of my
good fortune. You come highly recommended, Janina. I
have not seen the morning papers, but I've no doubt that by
now he will have tipped off his own gossip columnist and
that the news that you are with me will have permeated
along the grapevine.'

She bit her lip. 'And that's that, of course,' she said,
trying to infuse the right amount of sarcastic scepticism into
her voice. 'Once you've set your arrogant seal on a woman,
there's nothing more to be said.'

'I'll say this much,' he said quite gently. 'No one will
ever believe, *mia*, that I had you here against your will, although they will understand your motives for making such
a claim. But believe me, you are not the first—lady to en-
liven a vacation of mine.'

He was not boasting, just stating a fact, and there was no
reason at all why hearing the words from his own lips
should have cost her a pang, but it did.

'Nor,' he added quite gently, 'is it the first time for
you, *cara*, so let us play no more games. Be honest—in
other circumstances, this little interlude could have been
enjoyed by us both. As it is . . .' He shrugged.

'You're vile!' she whispered. If she had been flushed
before, she was now as pale as death.

His eyes hardened. 'Don't let us start calling names
either. At best it's unprofitable. Besides, I have far more
names for you than you could ever imagine for me.' He
rose to his feet in one lithe movement and stood looking
down at her. In spite of herself, Juliet shrank and her hands
gripped the sheet until the knuckles showed white. He saw
the instinctive movement and smiled rather grimly.

'Don't worry, *cara*. As I was going to say—as it is, I

wouldn't soil my hands with you, so you have nothing to
fear.' He turned away. 'And now I'll tell Annunziata to
bring you some coffee. You look as if you could do with
some kind of stimulant.'

Dry-mouthed, she said, 'How can I be sure it's safe for
me to drink?'

'It's safe.' He gave her an ironic glance. 'I have no
Borgia blood, *mia*.'

'But you drugged me,' she said tonelessly. 'You drugged
me and brought me here, and now you're going to keep me
prisoner, and you really think you're going to get away with
it.'

'You were hardly drugged,' he said coolly. 'A harmless
sleeping pill, that was all—a brand that my mother has
taken for some time without ill effects. And—yes, Janina,
I do think I'm going to get away with it. What you say
about me, what you do when you leave here is immaterial.
My only concern is that you do not marry my brother,
and he will not stoop to pick up what he will believe are
my leavings. Nothing else matters to me. But if you are so
foolish as to cry your woes to the world, then I leave it to
you to judge whose account of these events is more likely
to be believed. I am not without influence, as you must
realise by now.'

'I realise a great many things,' she said, her heart thudding so hard that it was incredible that he did not hear it.
'And now have the goodness to get out of my room.'

He gave her a long mocking look from the doorway.
'Something else for you to realise, *cara*,' he said almost
carelessly. 'This is not your room. It is mine.'

And on that, he disappeared.

Juliet searched wildly for words to fling after his retreat-
ing figure, but none came to her. When a moment or two
had passed and she was sure that he was not coming back,

she turned over, buried her face in the softness of the pillow and gave way to her overcharged emotions.

There was little point in telling herself that she could have avoided all this simply by telling him her real identity. It was too late for those sort of recriminations now. Here she was, and here she would stay until, presumably, he decided she had been here long enough, or discovered his mistake.

She shivered as she lay, her wet face pressed against the softness of the pillow. In many ways the whole escapade had started out as a game of chess, in which she, the white queen, was going to triumphantly overcome the arrogant black king. Now she knew bitterly that she had merely been a pawn all along. A fierce gladness rose within her at the knowledge that at least Jan had escaped him. No matter what humiliation she herself had suffered at Santino's hands, nothing could take away the fact that he had ultimately lost. Jan and Mario were safe from his machinations at least for the time being. What kind of married life they would have if they were to live perpetually in the shadow of his disapproval, she did not dare guess at.

Anyway, it was all so unnecessary and unfair. What, really, did he know about Jan? Not even enough to enable him to distinguish her from her sister. It followed therefore that his low opinion of her must be based on hearsay, and there was no justice in that.

Juliet lifted herself up on to an elbow, scrubbing the remaining tears from her eyes with a childish gesture. Well, even pawns had their place in a chess game, she reminded herself, and there would be an immense satisfaction in seeing his face, all his arrogance and power deflated, when he learned how sadly all his carefully laid plans had gone awry. Any humiliation she had suffered would be repaid in full on that day, she told herself fiercely.

She glanced towards the door. It was not even closed

now, let alone locked, as if he felt he had won already. Well, he would discover his mistake soon enough! She stiffened as she heard the sound of approaching footsteps, then relaxed again as she realised she was hearing the unmistakable shuffling of slippers, and not Santino's quick stride.

A moment later a woman appeared in the doorway. She was a plump soul dressed in the ubiquitous black, her thick grey hair dragged back into an untidy bun. She carried a tray of the promised coffee, and her plump olive-skinned face wore a broad grin. Dark, twinkling eyes candidly assessed Juliet as she approached the bed.

'*Buon giorno, signorina. Comé sta?*' she greeted her.

'*Benissima,*' Juliet replied with as much sarcasm as she could muster, but it was entirely wasted, she saw with resignation as Annunziata's face threatened to split in two with her smiles. She nodded approvingly at Juliet as she placed the tray on the chest of drawers, and poured some coffee into the fine china cup.

'*Bella,*' she muttered as she handed Juliet the cup, and Juliet felt her colour rise under the older woman's all-encompassing glance.

She took a cautious sip at the coffee, but this time there was no underlying bitterness to warn her. It was hot and fragrant and just what she needed, and in spite of herself she found her spirits beginning to rise.

'*Grazie,*' she said, indicating the coffee.

Annunziata broke into a flood of animated Italian, and Juliet with a laughing shake of her head indicated that she did not understand. Annunziata's face fell slightly, but she soon made it clear that she did not consider a trivial language barrier any real obstacle to having a gossip with her master's latest and unwilling guest.

Though of course Annunziata would not appreciate the fact that she was unwilling, Juliet thought as she drank her coffee. It was quite plain what the other woman thought was the true state of affairs, and there wasn't the slightest hint of disapproval on her plump face as she stood gazing down benignly on the girl in the bed.

Juliet finished her coffee with a sigh of repletion and placed the cup back on the tray. The next thing to do, she decided, was obtain something to wear. Using her few words of Italian and a lot of sign language, she managed to ask Annunziata if she knew where her clothes were, and to her relief the other woman nodded excitedly, her eyes full of laughter as she expressed quite volubly and unmistakably to Juliet's embarrassment that she too in her youth had known so impatient and ardent a lover.

There was no point in arguing about the real facts, Juliet told herself resignedly. There was no way in which she could make herself sufficiently understood to disabuse Annunziata's mind of the notions that possessed it. There was little doubt in her own mind that she was far from being the first naked girl Annunziata would have brought coffee to in Santino's bed, and she did not care for the pang that this realisation cost her.

It was none of her business what Santino did, she told herself resolutely, except where she herself was directly concerned. And although she had been frightened and upset, and her Roman holiday had been spoiled, yet it seemed she had little more to fear from him than had already transpired. She might have to suffer his taunts, but that was all. What was it he had said? *I wouldn't soil my hands with you ...*' The remembered contempt in his voice chilled her in spite of the heat of the day.

It was not long before Annunziata returned, lugging with her a suitcase which Juliet recognised thankfully as her own. But when she was alone again and able to examine its contents, she found to her dismay that they were a curious amalgam of her own things and Jan's as well. The glimpse she had had of Jan's wardrobe, not to mention the dress she had worn the previous evening, had shown her quite plainly that their style of dressing now lay worlds apart. Jan's taste was more sophisticated and daring in every way, and Juliet groaned as she examined some of the garments which would have to see her through the next few difficult days.

She had no idea how long her enforced stay with Santino was going to last. As she had expected, there was no sign of her bag, with the precious wallet containing her passport and money, and she was not silly enough to imagine she could hope to get anywhere without them.

The best policy—indeed the only one under the circumstances—seemed to be to sit this thing out. Sooner or later, she reasoned, Mario would be in touch to tell his brother that his marriage was now a *fait accompli*, and after that there would be no reason for Santino to detain her any longer. Unless he was so angry with the deception that he murdered her and dumped her body in the bay, she thought detachedly. One thing was certain, she could not imagine him being a good loser.

At last she chose, almost in desperation, a pair of flared denim pants with a brief matching waistcoat, which was slightly more substantial than the majority of the tops that had been included, and thrust her arms into a flimsy cotton peignoir which did belong to her, while she searched for a bathroom.

She didn't have far to look. Two doors away she found a massive bathroom with correspondingly massive marble furnishings. The only concession to modernity, apart from the hot water and the abundance of large fluffy towels, was the shower cabinet in the corner, and Juliet made full use of it, revelling in the splash of the cool water on her body. She dried herself slowly and thoroughly, before sampling some of the range of toiletries displayed on a wide shelf above the handbasin. Some of the most famous names in the French perfume industry were among them, and every possible choice of scent from light floral fragrances to the spicier, musky perfumes. Luxuriously smoothing toilet water over her shoulders and arms, Juliet thought idly what an incredible variety there was, and then paused, the colour rising in her face as she realised the perfumes and powders had been placed there to appeal to a variety of women.

She replaced the cap on the spray she had been using with indecent haste and replaced it on the shelf. She had little doubt that Santino had selected the perfumes himself, for his own delectation as well as that of his lady friends. She only hoped that he would not imagine she had been perfuming herself for him.

'I wish I'd used carbolic!' she muttered to herself, as she dragged the denims up over her slim hips and fastened the zip.

Once dressed, she felt rather at a loss. She stripped the covers back from the bed and left it to air, then emptied the suitcase and repacked it more neatly. Santino on his rampage through Jan's wardrobe had simply tossed things in on top of each other. Many of the things needed hanging up to rid them of creases, but ever present in her mind was Santino's parting shot that this was his room. There was no way in which she was going to lay even the slightest claim to it after that, even to the extent of hanging a few dresses in that huge wardrobe.

She wandered restlessly over to the window and stood looking out. Below her the sea shone like glass and the distant horizon shimmered in the heat. What was she supposed to do? she wondered. Stay here cooped up until Santino discovered the truth? She bit her lip. Not if she knew it, she told herself resolutely. After all, there was the sea, and where the sea was, there ought to be a beach of sorts. She would simply carry on with her holiday and to hell with Santino. After all, a lot of people paid hundreds of pounds to come and spend a few days on the Italian coast, and yet here she was being entertained at his expense in surroundings she could never have afforded in the ordinary way, so the least she could do was try and enjoy it.

She swung away from the window and went across to the door and out on to the gallery beyond. She trod across it and stood looking over the exquisitely carved balustrade that bordered it down into what was presumably the main living area below. It appeared deserted, and after a moment or two she ventured down the spiral staircase that led down from her side of the gallery, and stood looking about her. It was a large, lofty room, the floor smoothly tiled in a deep terra-cotta shade, the rough stone walls washed in pale cream. On one side a large alcove, with a slightly raised floor, had been let into the thickness of the wall and Juliet saw that this accommodated a large, heavily carved refectory table, and high-backed chairs padded in deep crimson. There appeared to be no fireplace as such, but the three long low oatmeal-coloured sofas which formed the seating were grouped round a low antique table, on which books and magazines were arranged. The original window recesses had been extended and glazed to make full use of the view, and a door behind her, under the gallery she had just left, indicated that this was where the kitchen quarters were to be found.

There was a spartan simplicity about her surroundings that appealed to Juliet far more than the more obvious luxury of Jan's Roman apartment. She wondered how old the building was, and admired the way it had been adapted to modern living needs without the destruction of its essential character. For it must have been some kind of fortress, she thought, her eyes straying once again to the thickness of the walls.

She wandered across the room, her heelless sandals

making little noise on the tiles, and picked up one of the magazines, but apart from the language problem they all appeared to be of a purely technical nature, so she soon abandoned that as a pastime. Presumably Santino's plans for the entertainment of his women guests did not include the provision of reading matter, she thought ironically.

Her stomach rumbled suddenly and disconcertingly, reminding her that it was a long time since she had eaten. She had enjoyed the coffee Annunziata had brought, but now she needed solid food inside her. Presumably as she was no longer a prisoner in her room, Santino did not plan to starve her either. Moodily, she flung herself down on one of the sofas and stared into space, wondering among other things where Mario and Jan were at that moment. She hoped they were happy, because that was the only thing that would make this entire business in any way tolerable. For a moment she felt tears prick at her eyes, then angrily dammed them back. It was useless indulging in self-pity. She had got herself into this mess, and she would simply have to get herself out of it in due course, and pray that she remained unscathed in the process.

As she lay back against the cushions, her eyes closed, struggling to regain her composure, she was suddenly aware that she was not alone. Her eyes flew open and she saw Santino standing over her. She sat up instantly, pushing her hair back with one defensive hand, hoping she had not exhibited any visible sign of weakness to him.

'I'm surprised to find you still indoors,' he observed after a moment or two of rather taut silence had stretched between them. 'Or are you afraid that our warm Calabrian sun will burn and blister that lovely skin?'

She shrugged a shoulder, thankful that he had mistaken the normal pallor engendered by a rather damp English summer for the care a model girl would lavish on her complexion.

'It is my livelihood after all, *signore*,' she replied in a small, cold voice.

He sat down beside her on the sofa, stretching his long legs in front of him, his lips twisting cynically as he looked at her. 'And in more than one way, *cara*,' he said softly, and laughed at her small, indignant gasp.

Her hand swung up to strike him, to smash the sneer from his face, but he was too quick for her. Cruel fingers seized her wrist and held it until she gasped again, this time in pain.

'I think not, *bella mia*,' he said between his teeth. 'Or I should be forced to exact retribution in a way that I promise you you would not like.'

'Simply being in the same room with you, *signore*, is quite punishment enough, believe me,' she said bitterly, nursing her wrist where the marks of his fingers showed red against the whiteness of her skin.

'*Veramente?*' His brows rose mockingly. 'Then I shall have to think of something to make your enforced sojourn in my home slightly less of a penance to you, Janina.'

'And to yourself, no doubt,' she said tartly.

He smiled. 'Oh, I don't regard you as a penance, Janina,' he said. 'For a man, there must always be compensations in the presence of a beautiful woman.' He reached out a lazy hand and took her wrist which she was still rubbing, raising it in one sensuous movement to his lips. 'You bruise easily, *cara*,' he murmured. 'That is something I shall have to remember.'

For a moment she was speechless, stunned by the obvious implication in his smiling words, then with a little choked cry she snatched her wrist away, trying to ignore the long tremor that had invaded her body at the pressure of his mouth against her flesh. For a second she was tempted to put the length of the sofa between them—he was so close to her that she could feel the warmth of his body, his thigh brushing hers as he lounged very much at his ease—but she knew that any such action would merely result in her looking foolish and undignified. But at the same time she would have to make it more than clear that she was not his plaything, no matter what role the other women who accompanied him here might fulfil.

'I'd prefer you not to touch me,' she said at last with what she gauged to be the right amount of ice in her voice.

'Why not?' he said, sounding faintly amused. 'There are no cameras or gaping crowds of avid clothes buyers here for you to pamper and perfume your body for, and yet your skin feels like silk and smells of sun-warmed roses. As your sole audience, I'd thought it might have been for my benefit.'

'Well, it isn't,' she replied stonily, hating herself for the faint involuntary blush that was creeping up under her skin at his words. Jan, she thought rather bitterly, would never have blushed no matter how personal the compliment might have been.

He laughed softly, but there was a faintly curious expression in his eyes, as if her reaction had bewildered him, and she tensed slightly. She certainly didn't want to arouse any suspicions about her identity now at this stage in the game. Even now it might not be too late for him to track down Mario and Jan and prevent their marriage.

She made herself relax back against the cushions, smile a little even.

'I'm a creature of habit,' she said, forcing herself to speak lightly. 'I assumed the perfumes and lotions were there to be used. Was I wrong?'

'On the contrary, *cara*.' He laced his fingers behind his head and leaned back, very much at his ease, the tawny eyes almost slumbrous as they studied her. 'I hope my choice of wardrobe for you was—adequate?' His gaze came to rest on the deeply slashed neckline of the skimpy waist-coat.

Juliet lifted a casual shoulder as if oblivious of his regard. 'I'll manage. After all, it won't be for very long, will it?'

'Who knows?' he murmured. 'Perhaps the charms of Roccaforte will appeal to you so much that you will decide to extend your stay.'

The charms of Roccaforte or its owner? she asked herself silently, her temper flaring under the sting of his arrogant presumption.

'I doubt it,' she said coolly. 'You can't imagine that I would willingly spend any more time in your company than necessary, *signore*?'

He laughed, apparently unmoved by the hostility in her tone. 'You would be surprised at the lengths to which my imagination can take me, *bella*. Although at times it does require a little practical assistance.'

Before she could anticipate his intention, he leaned forward and unfastened the top button of her waistcoat. 'I'm sure that was what the designer intended,' he added, his voice wickedly amused.

Her immediate impulse was to refasten the errant button and hide once again that provocative view of the shadowy cleft between her breasts that it afforded, but again she was forced to hesitate. Such an action would once more be uncharacteristic of Jan, she was forced to admit to herself. That kind of teasing byplay would be second nature to her. She wouldn't be sitting, her back ramrod-stiff, her cheeks flaming, every unsteady pulse beat in her body reminding her of the way his fingers had rested momentarily against the softness of her skin.

This is madness, she told herself flatly. She'd been kissed before—held, touched, so why had this man the power to inculcate such a response from such a fleeting contact? It didn't make sense. All she knew was this desperate, almost searing consciousness of his close proximity and the havoc it was playing with her logic, her reason, even her sense of decency. She even found herself wondering what it would be like if he kissed her—if that firm mouth would lose the slight sneer it wore so often and soften into tenderness just before it descended on hers...

With a desperate effort she tore herself away from the danger of that particular reverie.

'Don't fight so hard against your instincts, *cara*,' the mocking voice at her side advised her coolly. 'Mario is lost to you anyway, so there is nothing to be gained in withholding your body from me.' He reached out a hand and took her stiffly averted chin, forcing her head round so that she was facing him. 'Shall I tell Annunziata to spare herself the trouble of preparing another room, Janina *mia*?' His hand slid tantalisingly down the line of her throat, stroking the smooth line of her shoulder before continuing downwards to discover and explore softer curves. He frowned a little as his fingers encountered the barrier of denim, and Juliet gave a little choking cry as yet another button gave way under his seeking hands.

'No!' She snatched at the gaping edges of the waistcoat and held them across her breasts protestingly.

'Why not?' he demanded softly. 'I may not be about to offer you marriage like my ill-advised young brother, but you will not find me ungenerous, I promise you. Why defer something that we both know is inevitable?'

Juliet shook her head violently. She lifted her chin and stared at him, her eyes blazing with defiance.

'I don't doubt you have it all worked out, *signore*,' she said with only the faintest tremor in her voice to suggest she was not in complete control of the situation and her own emotions. 'But one thing you seem to have left out of your calculations is the fact that I find both you and your insulting advances totally abhorrent!'

The silence that followed her reckless words was electrifying. In spite of her bravado, Juliet felt a *frisson* of nervousness run the length of her body as she met his glance. There was anger there, but she had been expecting that— anger and something else that she could not immediately analyse.

'So you find me abhorrent, do you, *cara*?' he said at last, each slow word dropping like a stone into the tension between them. 'That's a lie, and you know it as well as I do, and if it weren't for the fact that Annunziata will be serving our lunch at any moment, I would prove that it was a lie here and now—to the ultimate satisfaction of us both,' he added, his insolent appraisal raking her from head to foot.

He rose and before she could guess his intention, leaned down, jerking her to her feet beside him. Then, while she was still off balance, his other arm went round her, pulling her against the warmth of his body, making her totally aware of his vibrant masculinity.

For one long earth-shaking moment he held her, letting her recognise the potency of his strength against her weakness. Then his hand went up to tangle in her hair while his mouth descended slowly and inexorably on hers.

Juliet couldn't breathe, she couldn't think, although at one point she thought she heard herself give a slight whimper. But if Santino heard it, he was plainly unmoved by it. His grip didn't slacken, nor did his relentless onslaught on her mouth. It was only the sheerest effort of will that kept her arms at her sides, when every instinct, every throbbing nerve ending in her body was shrieking at her to slide her hands up around his neck, to draw him closer still if that was possible—to tacitly acknowledge that he had the surrender he was seeking.

When at last he let her go, she could taste blood, and her hand came up almost of its own volition to cover her swollen mouth. Santino looked down at her and his eyes glowed oddly—like those of a mountain lion who has sighted his prey, she thought half-hysterically, and found herself praying that he would not touch her again.

As if in answer to her prayer, he stepped away to a low table near one of the window embrasures where bottles and glasses stood on a tray. He lifted one of the bottles and uncorked it, turning to where Juliet stood as if she had been turned to stone, his dark face cool and mocking.

'An *aperitivo, cara,*' he said, the faint amusement underlying his voice stressing the ambiguity of his words. 'To give us an appetite for the delicious meal to come.'

For a moment Juliet stared at him as he stood there, parodying the courteous host, then a long, slow shudder went through her and she turned away, forcing her unsteady legs to take her across the room to the stairs, and the fragile sanctuary of the room above. And as her hand fastened almost convulsively on the great iron latch of the door, she heard, as if in a dream, the echo of his laughter drift after her.

CHAPTER FIVE

JULIET sat disconsolately on the edge of the bed, staring down at the floor. Beside her were the remains of the lunch which Annunziata had brought her, somewhat reproachfully, on a tray. She herself had felt rather guilty at causing extra work, but it was either that or go hungry for there was no way in which she could have faced Santino Vallone across that shining table after what had passed between them.

No one in her life before had ever held her with such insolent intimacy or kissed her with such savage passion, she told herself shamedly, and it was not the slightest consolation to know that all that passion and brutality were not in fact intended for her, but for her sister.

She might be pretending to be Jan, but her response to

Santino's dark attraction from the very beginning had been all her own, and she had been a fool not to realise that a man of his experience with women would not have registered it, and reacted accordingly.

The last thing he would have expected was for her own reaction to have been that of a frightened virgin, she thought, the trace of an unwilling smile lifting the corner of her still-bruised mouth. And yet that was exactly what she was, and something she would never be able to disguise or pretend about.

She put up a hand and lifted the weight of her hair off the nape of her neck with a little sigh. This pitiful little charade of hers was running out of time fast, and she had little option, she felt, but to confess her real identity to Santino. It was not a confrontation she could look forward to with any sort of pleasurable anticipation. She now knew how he could be when he was angry, and it was not a state of mind she was anxious to provoke in him again.

In fact, she didn't really want to provoke him in any way at all, and one of her main priorities must be to get out of this room and into one of her own—preferably one with a lock on the inside—even if it was only one night, and she was forced to confess about her deception on the following day.

She got up and picked up her suitcase with determination. On the gallery outside, she paused, looking at the closed doors. The room next to Santino's was an empty bedroom, but she decided to avoid that particular one as being too close for comfort. Instead she chose a slightly smaller room on the far side of the bathroom she had used earlier. It was furnished in the same ruggedly magnificent manner as the rest of the *castello*, and only the bed needed making up. With the feeling that she would sleep fully dressed on the bare mattress if she had to, Juliet hastily staked a claim to her new lodging by unpacking her case.

Her next action was to make sure that the old-fashioned
bolt on the door really worked. It squeaked protestingly
as she pushed at it, but finally moved grudgingly along, and
she had to struggle once again to unbolt it. When she suc-
ceeded and opened the door, she was slightly disconcerted
to find Annunziata on the gallery outside, the used tray in
her hands, and her mouth hanging open in astonishment at
these goings-on by her master's latest guest.

When Juliet indicated that she would like to have the
bed made up, Annunziata's amazement and frank disbelief
were almost comical, and she immediately broke into a
flood of speech which Juliet had no difficulty in interpreting
as protests. It was clear Annunziata considered the occupa-
tion of an extra room a waste of time when it was clear, her
rolling eyes and gesticulating hands were saying, that
Juliet would be sharing Santino's bed.

It was perfectly obvious, Juliet thought resentfully, that
he had not bothered to give Annunziata any hint of the real
state of affairs between them. If only Annunziata spoke even
a few words of English, or she had Jan's fluency in Italian,
she could make the whole situation clear in moments, she
thought unhappily. As it was, Annunziata clearly believed
that some sort of lovers' tiff had taken place before lunch
which would all be happily resolved at bedtime, and as she
went off shaking her head, Juliet, watching her go, had no
great hopes that she would accede to her request and provide some bedding.

The view from this bedroom was slightly different, she
discovered. She could catch a glimpse of a silver-sanded
beach and some boats drawn up on it. She wondered if the
delicious fish she had eaten for lunch had been caught
locally. She decided she would go and explore later, when
she felt less comfortably full of food. She wandered back to
the bed and kicked off her heelless sandals, stretching herself full length on the mattress. She had closed the shutters,

and the room felt cooler without the full force of the sun pouring into it. The dim light was comforting too in its way, and Juliet found her eyelids beginning to sink involuntarily. She pulled herself together hurriedly. She wasn't going to sleep, just rest a little in the heat of the day, and presently she would put on one of the bikinis she had noticed had been included in her luggage and go down to that beach. In the meantime she would improve the shining hour by rehearsing some of her lines for the inevitable scene with Santino when she confessed who she really was.

It would be terrible if she stood in front of him, stammering and stuttering and totally at a loss. Far better if she had a speech all prepared, she thought, trying and discarding several promising opening gambits. Everything she thought of sounded either stilted or plain ridiculous, and her whirling thoughts had an oddly uncomfortable way of whisking her into a very different daydream in which she was telling Santino that she loved him.

'And that really is ridiculous,' she said aloud and very sleepily.

The next time she opened her eyes, it was to find Annunziata standing over her with an armful of bedding.

'Oh, heavens!' Juliet sat up stretching languorously. She was amazed to see from her wristwatch that she had slept for nearly two hours, and guessed she must still be suffering slightly from the aftermath of the sleeping tablet Santino had given her the previous night.

She helped Annunziata make up the big bed and gathered from her remarks that the older woman was surprised that the *signore* had given his permission for this to be done. Juliet was a little surprised herself, although she would not have allowed Annunziata to see this, and more than a little relieved. Perhaps Santino had decided to take her at her word, she thought without a great deal of conviction, as the memory of her unthinking response to that shat-

teringly demanding kiss returned to haunt her. It was far
more likely, she told herself uneasily, that he had decided
to play some sort of cat and mouse game of his own with
her. All she could hope was that he would allow this to
continue for at least twenty-four hours, by which time
Mario and Jan should be safely married and she could
make her confession. And when that was over, she thought,
Santino would probably never want to speak to her again,
let alone make love to her.

When Annunziata had gone off muttering and shaking
her head, presumably over the vagaries of young English-
women, Juliet changed swiftly into one of the bikinis. Once
again, it was far more revealing than she was used to, con-
sisting of little more than two semi-circles of jade green
cotton held together by strings for the bra top, and two
triangles tied at the side with strings for the bottom half.
Juliet gazed at herself in the full-length wardrobe mirror
and suffered a slight qualm when she saw just how much
of herself was going to be on show to the eyes of the
curious, and at the last minute she pulled on a white cheesecloth tunic with a rounded neckline and balloon sleeves.
Until she discovered how public the beach was, she told
herself defensively, pushing to the back of her mind the
thought that only one pair of masculine eyes was likely to
cause her any concern.

As she reached the ground floor and started towards the
great wooden door which gave access to the outside world,
she wondered for a moment if anyone would try to stop
her. Not that there seemed to be anyone about. Annunziata
had vanished, presumably back to the kitchen regions, and
Santino himself was nowhere to be seen. In a way, this was
something of an anti-climax. Juliet had been certain that he
would seek her out during the afternoon, and she had been
geared up for another confrontation between them. Now
she was conscious of feeling curiously deflated when her

overriding emotion should have been one of relief, she thought.

Outside the *castello*, the heat struck her like a blow, and she stood very still for a moment or two, getting acclimatised and assimilating her new surroundings. She could see now that the *castello* had been built on a rocky prominence at one end of a small bay. Just ahead of her, a long flight of stone steps cut into the side of the rock led down to the dusty ribbon of road along the shoreline, and below her she could see Santino's car drawn up in the shade of some trees.

Everywhere she looked seemed to shimmer in the heat. Along the bay she could see a cluster of roofs and white walls and guessed this was the village. Directly below the *castello*, the shore was rocky with infrequent patches of sand, but further along towards the village, Juliet saw that there was a gently shelving beach where a number of boats, many of them with curiously elongated prows, were drawn up.

Juliet made a slight grimace. If she wanted privacy, then it seemed that the rocky shore below the *castello* was her best bet. She did not particularly want to undertake her sunbathing under the gaze of any number of Italian fishermen. She shaded her eyes with her hand as she scanned the horizon and thought longingly of her new and expensive sunglasses left behind in Rome. She could feel the sun beating down on her unprotected head, and started forward down the steps. It might be slightly cooler down at the water's edge in between the rocks, she told herself.

As she reached the road, she cast a longing glance at Santino's car and on impulse crossed the small paved area into the shade of the trees to look at it more closely. Something in her mind was arguing half-heartedly that Santino *might* have left it unlocked with the keys in the ignition and a full tank of petrol, but even before the door catch resisted her tentative pressure, she knew she was being over-optimistic. Besides, even had her fantasy borne fruit, was she really planning to drive this sleek and powerful monster over roads she didn't know back to Rome? She shook her head regretfully and turned away. As she did so, something at one of the upper windows of the *castello* high above her caught her eye—a glint, as if the sun was being reflected back from glass that moved.

Indignation boiled up in her as she realised that some-one— and it had to be Santino— was watching her through binoculars. He must have seen her at the car, she thought furiously, and guessed what was going through her mind. Recklessly she turned to face the *castello* and thumbed her nose at it. It was schoolgirlish and silly, she knew, but it made her feel immeasurably better, and she marched on down to the beach with her head high and something approaching a swagger in her step. As she picked her way rather more gingerly across the stone and pebbles, she wondered if he was still watching her progress, but nothing in this world would have made her glance round to check.

It seemed, if possible, even hotter down on the shore and she moved more slowly, flinching a little as she clambered across rocks that had been baking in the sun for most of the day. At last she judged she was out of sight of the main rooms of the *castello* and without further hesitation she peeled off the cheesecloth tunic and dropped it beside the rock she was standing on, before diving in. The coolness of the water was a shock at first on her overheated body, but a delicious shock. For nearly twenty minutes she dived and swam and floated. The water was crystal clear, and she wished that she had a snorkel and mask so that she could explore the deep pools among the rocks even more thoroughly. She climbed back on to her rock and sat for a moment, wringing the water out of her sea-darkened hair, and feeling the damp scraps of her bikini drying perceptibly on her body in the heat. Beware of sunstroke, she thought, shaking her cloud of damp hair over the nape of her neck and covering herself rather regretfully with the cheesecloth tunic. In the distance she thought she could hear voices and guessed they were from the village, carried on the still air.

It was incredibly peaceful, she thought. Almost like Paradise—even down to having its own personal Satan lurking in the undergrowth. A reluctant smile twisted her lips as she visualised the arrogant Santino Vallone lurking anywhere. No serpentine subtlety in his make-up, yet he was as proud as Lucifer and had the face and bearing of a fallen angel.

Juliet sighed and gave herself a little mental shake. She was being fanciful again. Santino was no Prince of Darkness, she told herself roundly. He was simply a powerful industrialist who did not hesitate to take the law into his own hands if he deemed it necessary. The only pity was that she had had to experience his ruthlessness at first hand.

She rested her chin on one bent knee and stared broodingly across the glittering water, wondering what it must be like to encounter Santino under other circumstances—to know him as the other women who had stayed with him at the *castello* must have known him—as a casual acquaintance, then an escort, then a lover. She remembered moments over dinner the previous evening when he had seemed almost human, and she had recognised even then the pull of his attraction—moments when Jan's shadow had not been between them.

If I'd met him by chance, she thought, while I was sightseeing somewhere—the Colosseum perhaps, and he'd invited me to dinner—I wonder if I'd have accepted.

But she knew the answer to that particular question almost before her mind had framed it. Yes, she would have gone to dinner with him, and anywhere else he had chosen to take her, humiliating though the admission might be. It was as well for her own peace of mind that there had been this antagonism between them from the first. At least she still had some shreds of self-respect to hang on to.

Besides, she thought, reasserting her common sense, who's to say that if we had met casually somewhere, he would even have given me a second glance? The only reason she was here was because he was convinced that she was Jan, and he had probably only tried to make love to her because he was bored and she was available. She had no idea what kind of woman appealed to him, but she imagined someone as dark as himself, almond-eyed and sultry, or a ravishing Botticelli blonde.

She gave another little sigh. One thing was certain. When he and Jan did finally come face to face, he would ask himself how he could possibly have made such a mistake—would see how superficial the resemblance between them really was. She had seen it happen so many times over the years—heard herself described often as 'that lovely child' and then heard the intake of breath as the speaker's eyes fell on Jan, and know that once again she had been relegated to being 'the other one' or 'the quiet one'. She'd thought that it no longer had the power to hurt her, but suddenly she was fiercely resolved not to be around when the time came for Santino to make his comparisons.

She felt tears heavy and hot at the back of her eyes, and childishly pressed her balled fists against her eyelids.

Close beside her Santino's voice said, 'What's the matter?'

She started. She had been so absorbed in these new and painful reflections that she had never heard his approach.

'Nothing,' she said, sitting bolt upright and transferring her gaze back to the horizon with quite unnecessary intensity. 'The sun's a bit dazzling, that's all.'

'Have you no dark glasses?'

She shot him a fulminating glance. 'They were one thing you forgot,' she said too sweetly.

He gave her a mocking little bow. 'I suppose I may be forgiven one slight omission.' His eyes wandered over her, boldly assessing the slender curves revealed by the clinging cheesecloth. 'I seem to have chosen well in other respects.'

She shrugged one shoulder. 'If you want to think so ...' She resumed her intent scrutiny of the sea and the huge landmass which was just visible in the haze and heard him give a little half-suppressed sigh. It was an irritable sound, and she guessed he was not used to having his presence ignored in this way.

'You seem to find Sicily fascinating,' he observed.

'Is that Sicily?' She leaned forward, shading her eyes with her hand. 'I had no idea. I've never seen it before and ...'

'Never seen it?' He stared at her. 'I understood it was while you were working on a magazine spread near Palermo that you and Mario first met.'

Juliet swallowed. 'Well, of course,' she said after a moment. 'I simply meant that I'd never seen it from quite this angle before.' She gave a little artificial laugh. 'When you're working, one place is very much like another, you know.'

'I doubt that, *cara*,' he said a little grimly. 'Change places with a young girl labouring in a factory in Milan and see if she would agree with you.'

She flushed, already well aware of the foolishness of her remark. 'I didn't quite mean that,' she said stiltedly.

'I hope not.' His tawny eyes were narrowed as he looked at her. 'Do you know, you puzzle me, Janina.'

Her own glance fell away. 'I fail to see why,' she said in a subdued tone.

'I'll tell you why. Because you don't fit all my preconceptions. Most of them, *si*, but not all. There are—anomalies.'

Juliet could feel herself tensing. This is it, she told herself, the big denunciation.

She made herself pout a little. 'I'm sorry if I don't conform to the pattern of womanhood that you expected.'

'I didn't say that.' He smiled mirthlessly. 'In many ways you fulfil—all my expectations, and yet in others ...' He gave a slight shake of the head. 'I suppose it's all part of this artificial world you inhabit. Eventually you forget what it is to be a real person. Acting a role all the time must become second nature.'

So much for her skill in portraying Jan! She thought wryly.

'But I must confess, *mia*,' he went on, his voice deepening slightly, 'that occasionally in those great eyes of yours I catch a glimpse of someone I would like to know better.'

She could feel her heart beating very loudly and painfully. The impulse to tell him the truth there and then was almost overwhelming, but it was too soon, she told herself desperately. If the wedding hadn't taken place yet, there was still time for him to prevent it.

She gave a little tight smile. 'Has it ever occurred to you that it might be the same person that your brother Mario has fallen in love with?'

'No, it has not,' he said bitingly. 'I'm perfectly well aware of what constitutes your attraction for Mario, *cara*, and it is not your beautiful soul. In the early days, before you managed to persuade him that he needed to marry you, he was almost embarrassingly frank on the subject.'

A faint colour rose in her cheeks that she hoped fervently he would attribute to the sun.

'Then I'm surprised you didn't decide to nip the affair in the bud right then,' she said quickly, bending forward so that her hair swung in a concealing curtain across her cheek.

'Why should I? I told myself that Mario had as much right as anyone to sow some wild oats before settling down with a wife and family.' His voice was cynical. 'Where I made my mistake was in believing that you knew the rules of the game and were content to abide by them.'

'Aren't you afraid,' she said slowly, still staring down at the sun-bleached rock, 'that Mario will hate you for ever because of what you've done?'

'I don't doubt he will be a little angry at first.' He sounded faintly amused. 'But you flatter yourself, *cara*, if you imagine that you have the power to start a vendetta between us. Mario will be philosophical eventually. You have made him a delectable mistress, but all good things must come to an end, as he knows very well. He has family obligations to fulfil, and I'm sure it will be a weight off his mind to know that you are being—well looked after.'

'By you, I suppose,' she said, her voice shaking with anger. 'My God, if you only knew how I hated you— despised you!'

He laughed. 'It doesn't particularly disturb me, *bella mia*. A little hatred might prove a refreshing novelty. At least it means you won't bore me with endless protestations of un- dying love that we would both know were false.' He was silent for a moment, then he reached out and gripped her shoulder, pulling the thin covering of cheesecloth away from it. 'Don't let's fool ourselves, Janina,' he muttered thickly. 'There was something between us from the mo- ment we looked at each other. I knew it and so did you, so we'll forget the virtuous denials.' He bent his head, and she felt his breath warm on her neck. He ran his tongue slowly along the smooth curve of her shoulder and she felt a great shiver convulse the centre of her being.

'You taste of salt.' His voice was husky and close to her ear. 'You haven't a trace of make-up, and your hair is hanging in a hundred rats' tails, and if we weren't surrounded by these accursed rocks, I'd take you now.'

'Leave me alone!' she whispered wretchedly. She was close to tears and even closer to panic. It would be so easy to turn to him, to yield, to be drawn against the hard warmth of his body, but she knew if she gave way to any of the warm, treacherous impulses which had invaded her body then she would awake the next morning to shame and regret. Besides, if she gave herself to him, he would very soon know that it was not Janina whom he held in his arms. Juliet's painful lack of the kind of experience she had no doubt he would demand would soon reveal the trick that had been played on him, and although he had to find out eventually what she had done, she did not think she could bear for him to find out quite like that.

'Alone.' His tone was frankly sceptical. 'What is this sudden passion for solitude? Annunziata tells me you've insisted on having a bed made up in the guestroom. Are you afraid that she'll be shocked that you turn to me after my brother. She knows nothing of your involvement with Mario. She reads no newspapers—at least not the kind you feature in—and no gossip reaches her ears.'

'In fact to her I'm just another in a long line of your lady house guests—only not quite so accommodating,' she said flatly. 'Believe me, I'm not simply trying to make the situation acceptable to Annunziata. I'm trying my hardest to prove to you that it isn't acceptable to me.'

'Not acceptable?' His voice hardened. 'When I've felt your body tremble in my arms longing to yield me its last secrets? *Dio*, Janina, do you take me for some naïve fool on the brink of his first affair?'

'Oh, no,' she said bitterly. 'Not that—never that. But hasn't it ever occurred to you that simply wanting something—or being able to buy it even—isn't always sufficient justification for having it?'

For a moment there was silence, then he said grimly,

'You are a mass of contradictions, *mia*, as I indicated earlier. Very well—we will play the game your way, but the result will be the same in the end, and when I kiss you awake in my arms I defy you to tell me that you are sorry or—unjustified!'

'You make it sound utterly ridiculous,' she said wearily. 'I just can't convince you that I'm in earnest.'

'But so am I, *cara*,' he said very softly. 'So am I.'

She got to her feet, half afraid that he might detain her, but he remained where he was while she scrambled down from the rock and began to make her slow way back across the tumbled stones to the road. With every step she took, she was conscious of his eyes watching her, and it was much as she could do to stop herself from running.

She didn't want to look back at him, in fact she was determined not to, yet somehow, as she gained the uneven surface of the road which led to the *castello*, she found her steps faltering, and her head turning almost in spite of herself. He was still in the same place, a dark almost sinister figure stretched out on the rock, bleached white by the sun. As he saw her hesitation, his hand came up in a half-mocking salute and he rose to his feet.

For a moment Juliet thought he was coming after her and with a gasp, was poised for flight. Then she realised, as he tugged his shirt over his head, and unzipped his pants that he was only going for a swim.

He walked to the edge of the rock and stood motionless for a moment before diving in, and Juliet realised for the first time that he wasn't wearing trunks or in fact anything at all. She turned away hurriedly, feeling that betraying blush stealing into her face again, and began to walk, far more quickly than the heat of the day demanded, up the steps towards the *castello*.

Juliet stood looking at herself in the full-length cheval

mirror that stood in the corner of her room, a faint cloud
of doubt shadowing her face. In just a few minutes it would
be time for her to go downstairs to dinner, and she wanted
to be sure that her appearance was exactly right.

She'd dressed with a great deal of heart-searching that
night, choosing after some hesitation an evening dress
she had herself bought back in England and which by
chance had been included in the wardrobe that Santino
had so hastily assembled for her.

She had not been able to resist the dress when she saw
it in the boutique, but she had never imagined that she
would wear it under quite these particular circumstances.
It was made of a soft silky fabric, rather like chiffon, in an
entrancing shade somewhere between blue and green. The
neckline was low and boat-shaped, and the sleeves full and
transparent, and the full skirt billowed round her slender
legs as she moved. There was a long matching scarf, and
she had used this to tie back her hair.

The severity of the hairstyle and the fragility of the dress
combined to increase her air of vulnerability, and it was
this that disturbed her as she surveyed herself. She did not
want to look fragile and vulnerable. She wanted to look
composed—totally in command of the situation.

The dress was wrong for this too, of course, but the
alternative had been to wear yet another of Janina's, and
none of them appealed to her. They were all glamorous, and
clearly expensive, but their glamour was an obvious one—
designed to take the eye, and capture a man's attention.
The perfect clothes for the transient, brittle world that
Janina occupied, Juliet thought rather sadly.

And what was the point of attracting a man if you knew
at the same time that once his desire was satisfied there
would be nothing left but contempt?

Besides, she was by no means sure that she could continue acting the part of Janina even for a few hours longer.

The whole charade had become steadily more distasteful to her, and not even the thought that she was getting the better of Santino on her sister's behalf could alleviate that unhappy awareness.

She was coming to the conclusion from Santino's remarks—from his whole attitude—that there was a great deal about Jan, and about her life since she had started work in Italy, that she did not know about, and would have preferred to remain in happy ignorance of. Now that her eyes had been opened to a certain extent, she could only be thankful that Mim was still living in blissful innocence about Jan's lifestyle and general morality. All she could hope was that Santino was prejudiced enough against Jan to have exaggerated everything he thought and said about her.

Often, Juliet owned to herself rather dazedly, it was as if he was talking about a complete stranger, not the girl she'd been brought up with and thought that she knew.

She shook her head and saw the ends of the long scarf float out behind her as she did so. A little sigh broke from her lips. It was such a lovely dress—charming and romantic. A dress in which to dream dreams—a dress for love.

Only there was no love awaiting her downstairs in that lofty room which seemed to have been hewn out of the solid rock that the *castello* stood on. Instead there was a transient passion—a casual gratification of the senses, if she chose to accept it; a few hours, she knew, of a delight that she might never know again. But when it was over, what would remain? The commitment which could have transmuted that passion into a deeper, more lasting emotion was totally lacking. After Santino had possessed her, he would despise her, and when he discovered that she was not even the girl that he had intended to tame, to bring to heel, then he would despise her even more.

Juliet turned away from the mirror, her heart sick within her, but she felt she could delay no longer. The last thing she wanted was for Santino to come up to this shadowed room to seek her. It was altogether too intimate a setting for such an encounter, she thought, her pulses beating wildly, her eyes widening as they fell upon the bed, immaculately gleaming with freshly laundered linen, with a nightgown—one of her own, not Jan's—lying across the coverlet like a drift of snow.

She went slowly out on to the gallery and down the spiral stairs, lifting her skirt carefully out of the way of her feet as she descended.

Santino was standing by the window, gazing out into the gathering darkness, a glass in his hand. Juliet could have sworn she made no noise as she came down the stairs, but his head came round and he stared at her as she reached ground level.

'Would you like a drink?' he asked abruptly, his eyes going over her frowningly, as if he was having difficulty in registering who she was.

'A fruit juice, please,' she said, adding hastily as his frown deepened. 'I—I'm rather thirsty. It's been so hot today ...'

He fetched her the juice in a tall glass without a comment, and she sipped it, clasping her damp hands gratefully round the coolness of the ice-filled tumbler. She was conscious of a feeling of disappointment, and realised that childishly she had been hoping that he would tell her that she looked beautiful, or even that he would look more closely and know that she wasn't Jan, and that somehow all explanations would be unnecessary. Fool, she thought unsteadily.

The room was lit by lamps, and in the dining alcove Annunziata had set the candles burning in a magnificent candelabrum.

'It looks so right,' she murmured, half to herself, and flushed slightly as she encountered Sántino's questioning gaze. 'The candles, I mean, in that particular setting.'

'Are you a romantic, Janina?' His smile was slightly twisted. 'I wouldn't have thought it. Next you will tell me that you have started to fall in love with your prison.'

She wanted to say, 'Not with my prison, but with my jailer.' Instead she heard herself saying in a prim little voice, totally unlike her own, 'I've always been interested in history. I suppose the *castello* is very old.'

'*Si.*' The tawny eyes were mockingly alight, as if he knew why she was deliberately avoiding any subject of conversation which could be interpreted as personal. 'It was built orginally by the Saracens, I believe. Since then it has been destroyed and rebuilt several times, of course.'

'And have you lived here long?' She took another refreshing sip of her fruit juice, avoiding his direct glance.

'Long enough,' he said rather drily. 'It changed hands several times before I came on the scene. It needed a lot of work, and I think the prospect of the time and money it would take deterred many people from tackling the task.'

'But not you, of course,' she said, her own tone a little dry.

He smiled. 'It is true,' he said softly. 'From my earliest childhood, I dreamed that one day I would live in such a place. There was a plan to turn it into a hotel, which I was fortunately able to prevent.'

'Are you against tourism?'

'No, I think it could be of immense benefit in an area as poor as this has been, yet this *castello* is not big enough to make a successful hotel. I felt it would be better used as a private residence. But that has not stopped me joining a consortium of other business men who are building a chain of luxury hotels along this stretch of coastline.'

'It won't—spoil your dream to have to share it with

others?' she asked rather shyly, and he frowned again.

'Dreams are for children,' he said coldly. 'Only fools confuse them with life's realities.' He swallowed the contents of his glass in one gulp and moved back to replace it on the tray.

Juliet felt a kind of simmering anger emanating from him, but she had no idea what she could have said or done to have inspired it, but she remembered he had reacted in very much the same way on other occasions when she had attempted to get close to him, to find out what he thought and believed. It was further proof, if proof she needed, that his sole interest in her was physical. Her feelings, her emotions, her thoughts had probably never even entered his mind.

Santino didn't want any kind of intellectual stimulation from a woman, she thought sadly, he merely required a willing body to share his bed, and she was simply fooling herself if she imagined that her resistance to his attempts to make love to her would arouse either his interest or ultimately his respect. If he found he could not seduce her, then he would probably shrug his shoulders and write her off as a miscalculation. The fact that he had encountered a girl who wasn't willing to fall immediately into bed with him wouldn't impress him in the slightest. He would find it simply a trifling irritation, nothing more. In the days ahead, he wouldn't even regard the incident with a tinge of regret. He would regard that as sentimentality, fit only for children along with dreams.

He did not return to the sofa where she sat, her slim body stiff with tension, but remained standing by the window as he had been when she came downstairs. She found herself wondering precisely what his brooding gaze could be fixed on, because surely it was too dark to see anything now.

She was almost glad when a clatter at the door and quick

bustling movements announced the arrival of Annunziata with the soup. Once it was served, Annunziata did not leave right away, but stood watching them taste it, smiling warmly and proudly. She had every right to feel proud, Juliet thought, as she spooned up some of the thick hot liquid, redolent with meat and vegetables and herbs. It was good enough to be a meal in itself, and in a strange way she felt it was putting new life, new heart into her.

But at last Santino glanced up and said something to her. Juliet could not catch the words, which were uttered in a low voice, but she heard the tone, and although not unkind it was firmly dismissive, and Annunziata lost no time in making herself scarce.

Juliet bent her head over her plate, instinctively avoiding the glance of the man who sat confronting her across the flickering candles. Here in the dining alcove, they seemed curiously cut off from the rest of the *castello*, the thick walls closing intimately around them, the candles casting a pool of light which seemed to be the only reality, a charmed circle in which they were caught for all eternity.

For no reason, she found herself remembering that moth which had kept circling their table at the restaurant—was it only twenty-four hours ago? It seemed like a lifetime. The moth too had been drawn by that circle of light, she thought, drawn closer and closer towards disaster. It might so easily have blundered into the protective globe and died there, its wings singed irrevocably by the flame.

And was she any better than the moth? She was drawn too, but the flame that threatened to engulf her was the power, the attraction that she felt emanating from Santino —a flame that was capable of breaking down all her powers of resistance, her defences, and even her self-respect.

As if in a dream, she heard his voice asking her courteously if she had finished and realised, her face flaming, that she was sitting with her spoon suspended above an empty plate, transfixed by her thoughts and the quivering emotions that they were engendering.

He reached out and rang a small silver handbell which had been placed beside him, and Annunziata was quick to obey its summons. Watching her deftly remove the plates and bring the grilled sardines which formed the next course, Juliet thought with some bitterness that she must be well used to waiting for the sound of the bell. If it did not ring, she would know that her master and his guest would not want to be disturbed.

Studying her under her lashes, Juliet wondered what Annunziata must think of the frequent changes of female visitor. Was she shocked? She wore a silver crucifix at the neck of her plain black dress, so presumably she was a Catholic. But perhaps the wages that Santino paid her were sufficient to assuage her conscience. After all, as Juliet knew to her cost, he believed that everyone could be bought.

She forced herself to eat because she did not want Santino to guess at the confusion of thought and emotions that was preying on her mind, but she had no real appetite. She was only glad that he was not making conversation. Yet his silence was equally disturbing in its own way. Perhaps it was deliberate, she thought, pushing the crisp little fish unwillingly round her plate. Another ploy intended to rattle her, make her even more vulnerable than she was already.

The wine in her glass was cold and dry and she was glad of it, grateful for the warmth it seemed to spread through her veins. Annunziata came again, tutting a little over the amount Juliet left on her plate, her plump face anxious, but at the same time confident that the *signorina* would find the next course perhaps more to her taste. Juliet nodded and smiled as the chicken simmered with wine and cream and mushrooms was placed lovingly in front of her, but she was only too aware that mocking tawny eyes across the table were assessing her and probably knew as well as she did that her throat had almost closed with her nervousness, and that she would find it difficult to swallow even a bite of the deliciously fragrant concoction in front of her even helped down by the wine that was spreading such a false glow of confidence through her body.

Santino reached for the bottle and refilled her glass, lifting his own towards her.

'*Alla salute, cara,*' he murmured.

She raised her own glass in reply but said nothing. She wondered if it was significant that he had drunk to her health instead of a toast that would have bound them together, such as 'To us.'

As he turned to help himself from the heaped dish of broccoli spears which Annunziata had placed on the table, she studied him unobtrusively, taking the first long look at him that she had dared to since she had come downstairs.

He was wearing a faultlessly cut velvet dinner jacket in some dark colour—black, she thought, or maybe navy—and the shirt beneath it was white, elaborately frilled and beautifully laundered. Every last detail about his appearance spoke of money.

He glanced up suddenly and caught her eyes full on him. One eyebrow rose sardonically, but before he could ask the invitable question, she herself rushed into speech, a thought that had preoccupied her more than once finding utterance at last.

'Is it because my—I'm poor, because I have to work for a living that you don't want me to marry your brother?' Her haste had made her careless. She had nearly said 'my sister', and hoped he hadn't noticed the slip.

But he was plainly too astonished by the remainder of the question to pay any heed to that fleeting stumble over words.

'Are you trying to be funny?' he asked at last, contemptuously.

'No.' Juliet shook her head vehemently. 'It—it's just that I'm at a loss to understand why you're so opposed to the idea. You—you've never really told me the reason, you know—just left me to infer things from what you've said.'

'And the inferences you have drawn have not been clear to you?' He refilled his own glass, flicking the lace ruffle back from his wrist with a practised gesture. 'I'm sorry, *cara*, if I've been obscure. I thought we understood one another.'

'I'm not sure I understand anything any more,' she said wearily.

'Then understand this.' He laid down his fork and stared at her, the tawny eyes hard and curiously bright beneath the dark brows. 'I would never despise an honourable poverty. Do you imagine my family has always been wealthy? That I have always lived in surroundings such as this—had servants at my beck and call? You know nothing. What I have achieved has been done with these.' He extended his hands in front of him. 'Tomorrow I will take you to the village, Janina, and you will see the house where my father was born. You will ask yourself how anyone could survive in such a place, let alone bear and raise a family.'

'Were you born there too?' Juliet asked almost timidly.

He shook his head. 'I first saw the light of day in the slums of Reggio,' he said tiredly. 'A beginning that has even less to recommend it than a hovel in Roccaforte. You need a will to survive there too, *bella mia*, and that's what I had—a will and a passion to learn that by some miracle was recognised.' He leaned back in the high carved chair, the sudden emotion dying out of his face, leaving it dark and enigmatic again. 'Has Mario told you nothing of this?' he demanded.

She shook her head, hoping that he would not press for any further explanation of Mario's obviously unexpected reticence.

He smiled coldly. 'He must have believed that his present good fortune would have been more acceptable to you, *cara*, than his humble beginnings.' His voice bit. 'Not that his struggle was ever overwhelming. As he was so much younger, his path was made easier by my own early successes. Perhaps too easy.'

'Will you please get it into your head that I am not after Mario for his money!' she said hotly. Oh, Jan, let it be true, she thought agonisingly.

He shrugged a shoulder. 'I believe you. Why not? There have been richer men in your life, *cara*, as I am sure you don't mind admitting as you are urging me to speak frankly. But Mario, being young and a fool, was the only one who offered marriage, wasn't that it, Janina? A young, wealthy husband and instant respectability was what you opted for. I do not altogether blame you. In your own rather permissive little circle you must have been becoming rather notorious. Mario must have seemed like a lifeline tossed to a drowning man, only I'm afraid I am going to have to let you drown, because my plans for Mario do not include his marriage to a *puttana* like you.'

She cried out—even her scanty knowledge of Italian was sufficient to translate that term for her—and before she could recapture her self-control she flung the contents of her wine glass straight in his face.

'*Dio!*' He was on his feet, reaching furiously for a table napkin, dabbing at the spots of wine marking his once immaculate shirt and jacket, mopping the rivulets of liquid that were running down his face.

Juliet sat as if she had been turned to stone, waiting for the moment when he would turn his attention to her. There was something inherently comical in someone having something thrown all over him, so why was it she had never felt less like laughing in her life?

He picked up the handbell and rang it imperiously, his fingers closing round the fragile silver stem as if it was her neck, swearing softly under his breath as he did so.

When the flustered Annunziata arrived almost at the gallop, he gestured to her to clear the table. He offered no explanation, but Juliet thought Annunziata would easily be able to draw her own conclusions from the soaking tablecloth and Santino's own suddenly dishevelled appearance.

She sat and looked down at her fingers linked tensely together in her lap. She was ashamed now of what she had done, but it had been an instinctive reaction. She could not have sat quietly by and heard Janina labelled as a prostitute. She felt cold and sick inside.

Santino walked round to her side of the table and his fingers hurt as they closed around her wrist, jerking her to her feet.

'Red hair,' he observed too pleasantly. 'I should perhaps have realised that somewhere there would be a temper to match it.'

'I'm sorry,' she said, biting her lip to conceal the pain she was feeling from his crushing grip. 'But you shouldn't have said that.'

'It was you that wanted to hear the truth,' he said coldly. 'And you will be sorry, I promise you.'

He pushed her down on to one of the sofas, sat down beside her and before she could pull away or utter a protest, his arms were round her pulling her against him and he was silencing her indignant mouth with his own.

He was very thorough and very brutal, but only Juliet was aware that it was anger not passion that was driving him. To Annunziata, scuttling from the room with the debris from the table, it would simply have seemed as if the *signore* was re-establishing his mastery after some lovers' tiff.

The weight of his body was pressing her inexorably back against the soft cushions. Her hands had come up between them instinctively in an attempt to push him away, but it was useless. Against the demand of his lips and hands, she had all the resistance of a rag doll. Her fingers were splayed against the dampness of his shirt front and she could feel the warmth of his skin through the thin material. Somewhere inside her a small wanton voice was urging her to unfasten the buttons of his shirt and slip her hands inside, to touch the warm muscularity of his chest.

He lifted his head and stared down at her, and although he was still frowning, she knew that much of his anger had already been dissipated in that first furious assault on her mouth.

When he bent to her again, his kiss, his touch had magically gentled. This time his lips barely brushed hers before moving on to caress the curve of her cheek, her temples, her half-closed eyes. And at once that old traitorous longing rose up within her to betray her, roused by this new and unexpected tenderness.

Santino pressed his lips along the smooth line of her jaw and lingered over the telltale pulse in her throat, while his hand gently and rhythmically stroked the curve of her bare shoulder.

Juliet felt a little shaken sob rise in her throat. His hands and mouth were unbearably persuasive and her own response was little short of tumultuous. The restraint he was showing was a provocation in itself, and she was shamingly aware that her body was straining upwards to meet his in an unspoken offering, her rounded breasts straining against the flimsy material which imprisoned them, the nipples taut with desire.

He stared at her again, his eyes studying her mouth as if

he had undertaken to commit its soft fullness to memory. His hands were busy at the nape of her neck, unfastening the scarf that confined her hair so that it fell in a tangled coppery cloud on to her shoulders. Then he bent and kissed her again, parting her lips with intimate possession and awakening her to a greater sensual awareness of what a kiss could be than she had ever known before.

When at last he lifted his head, she heard herself give a little involuntary moan of protest, and he laughed, deep in his throat.

'Don't be impatient, *cara mia*.' His voice was deeper and huskier than she had ever heard it. 'We have all the night ahead of us, and besides, I want to dance with you—a pleasure I've promised myself for a long time.'

He slipped the scarf round her waist and holding both ends in one hand pulled her gently, almost teasingly to her feet.

Dance? she thought bewilderedly. But there's no music.

As if he had read her thoughts, he led her over to an intricately carved chest at one side of the room and pressed some hidden switch. At once music swelled into the room from concealed speakers, very soft and slow with an insidious sensuous beat. He let the scarf drift to the floor and slid his arms around her, drawing her close, making her move with him to the music.

For a dazed moment she thought that this was what she had dreamed about when she had first seen this dress. She had known instinctively that it was a dress to fall in love in, and she knew now that in spite of everything that had happened, everything that had been said, she had fallen in love with Santino Vallone. She let herself relax against his body, leaning her head against his shoulder, while his arms tightened possessively round her.

She could, she thought, have stayed like that for ever, but laughing softly he pushed her away to arm's length, spinning her gently so that the long delicate skirt floated out around her like a blue-green cloud, then drew her back so that he could kiss her again. Nothing mattered, she thought, closing her eyes, but the sheer intoxication of his nearness.

His lips found the sensitive hollow just below her ear, and she heard him whisper, 'Dance for me, *mia*. I want to watch you.'

Opening her eyes, she found the room was much darker than it had been. While they were dancing, Santino must have been extinguishing the lamps one by one. But he had retained one of them, a tall standard lamp which spilled a pool of light on to the tiled floor rather as a spotlight might do upon a stage, and this presumably was where he wanted her to dance, because he had stepped back into the shadows and was standing watching her.

She felt suddenly shy and a little foolish. She was no dancer, but no one could have resisted the beat of that music. It was strangely lonely in the pool of light as she began to sway to it, using her shoulders and hands first, then her hips and the whole of her body, the rhythm seeming to take over and become a part of her. Her whole body felt light as air and she lifted her skirts in each hand, using the fullness as if they were butterfly wings as she dipped and swayed and turned in time to the beat.

But she wasn't a butterfly, she thought dreamily as she spun round. She was a moth circling endlessly in the brightness, utterly possessed by its brilliant, dangerous excitement.

Santino was behind her suddenly. His hand lifted the heavy fall of hair away from her neck and his lips were burning on her nape.

'Exquisite, *mia cara*,' he murmured against her ear. 'But not quite what I intended. I wanted you to dance for me as

you danced at Vittoria Leontana's party. You can't have
forgotten. Or shall I refresh your memory?'

His fingers stroked down her bare back until they
reached the edge of her dress, then continued, taking the
long zip fastener with them. The gown slipped from her
shoulders and slid to the floor at her feet in a shimmering
pool.

For a moment Juliet stood still, shocked and motionless,
then with a stifled cry she bent and snatched up the dress,
holding its folds protectively against her bare breasts as he
turned her inexorably to face him. His eyes narrowed impatiently as he observed her instinctive gesture of modesty.

'Why bother to pretend any more?' he asked. 'You didn't
cover yourself before me—or nearly thirty others—at
Vittoria's party, although your outraged escort intervened
before the ultimate revelation.' He smiled reminiscently, but
the smile did not reach his eyes which remained curiously
hard as they studied the girl in front of him, who might
have been some piece of ancient Roman statuary of a god-
dess, clutching her flimsy draperies about her, except for
the ebb and flow of colour in her cheeks which marked her
as being all too human.

'I don't know what you mean,' she managed at last past
the tightness in her throat.

'Don't you? Yet it was a memorable performance. It
made an indelible impression on me, *cara*, and I was only
privileged to see the last few minutes of it. But I was told
afterwards that when it was realised you were not only
prepared to take off your dress but everything else beneath
it, you could feel the shock waves on the Via Veneto.' He
smiled without mirth. 'Striptease is not new, of course, but
it has a certain rarity value when performed in a usually
respectable *salotto*. Nor, I believe, does the dancer normally
distribute her garments as so much largesse among her
audience.' He paused. 'Poor Rizziani was most upset,' he

continued almost casually. 'I thought at the time he was probably disturbed to find that your charms were not reserved for his eyes only as he had probably thought, but I think now he was probably equally concerned at the cost of the clothes you had discarded so carelessly, and which he had presumably paid for.'

The calm voice stopped, and Juliet found her legs buckling under her as if only the necessity to hear what he had to say had been keeping her upright. She sank to the floor, her hands still gripping her crumpled gown so tightly that the knuckles showed white. Bowing her head, she began to cry, long tearing sobs that hurt her throat, painful tears that scalded her eyes.

He wasn't lying, even though her mind rejected the pictures his words had evoked. He spoke so coolly, so passionlessly, but then he had no idea that he was destroying an illusion. Janina—the spoilt, the beautiful, the envied. Juliet's blood went cold within her as she visualised her mother's stricken reaction if this ever came to her ears. Mim mustn't know, she thought wildly. The baby was nothing compared to this. Mim could have understood that, probably, although she would have been hurt. But Mim would never, never understand how a daughter of hers could have deliberately stripped naked to titillate the jaded palates of a handful of Roman society partygoers. And from what Santino had said, it seemed that Jan had at the time been the mistress of this Rizziani, whoever he was. It was all so degrading, so much worse than she could ever have suspected even in her wildest nightmares. Was it any wonder than Santino Vallone balked at the idea of Jan marrying into his family? Could she entirely blame him for his opinion of Jan, knowing what he knew, seeing what he had seen?

'The tears are charming.' His voice cut cynically across her desperate thoughts. 'But it's a little late for remorse,

cara. And I'm not as old-fashioned as Rizziani. I don't believe that a beautiful girl should necessarily be anyone's
exclusive property. And you are beautiful—hair like fire
and a body like snow, an intriguing combination. I always
hoped I would have the opportunity to see them again. And
tonight you can complete the performance. There'll be no
Rizziani to interrupt with his tiresome objections or wrap
his coat around you just at the moment of truth this time,
so dry your eyes, *mia*, and go on with your dance.'

'I can't.' She pressed a fist against her trembling lips.
'You—you don't understand ...'

'I think I do.' He reached down and lifted her to her feet,
not gently. His eyes glittered in the lamplight which
shadowed the dark planes and angles of his face, making
him look more satanic than ever. 'In spite of the broad hint I
gave you at our first meeting, *piccina*, you still didn't really
believe I'd seen you myself, did you? And it isn't pleasant
to be found out in one's misdeeds, especially when one
thought they were buried for ever. But why so coy, *mia
cara*? If I'd undressed you a few moments ago while we
were kissing, you wouldn't have uttered a protest.'

His hand closed over the thin folds of material she was
still clutching to her breast.

'Such a pretty dress,' he said pleasantly. 'Don't make me
tear it off you, my lovely one.'

It took every ounce of strength that she possessed to enable her to step backwards, striking his hand away from her
as she did so. His face darkened with anger and he took a
quick stride towards her, then halted, obviously puzzled by
the look of open desperation in her pale tear-stained face.

'What is it?' he demanded. 'Janina *mia*, I won't ...'

'Don't call me that,' she interrupted. Her voice was low
but it throbbed with an angry sincerity which brought his
dark brows together in an incredulous frown. 'And don't
touch me either. In fact, once I've said what I have to say,

I only pray I'll never have to see you or speak to you again.'
She paused and took a deep breath. 'I've—I've been lying to
you, *signore*, right from the first. I'm not Janina Laurence.
I'm Juliet, her older sister from England.'

CHAPTER SIX

JULIET stood waiting tensely for the inevitable explosion of
wrath. She had totally convinced herself that this was how
he would react when at last she had to tell the truth, so his
shout of laughter, harsh and jeering, was a shock which
sent her startled gaze flying in disbelief to his face.

'Your fairy stories are no doubt delightful, *mia cara*,' he
said. 'But this is neither the time nor the place to indulge in
them. You are beginning to try my patience.'

He took another step towards her. There was menace in
every lean, muscular line of his body and Juliet felt herself
cringing inwardly, aware of a cowardly desire to turn tail
and run. Yet at the same time she knew she had to stand
her ground and convince him somehow that she was speaking the truth.

'No, you must listen,' she said rapidly. She had backed
away from him as far as she could and was now trapped by
the high back of one of the sofas just behind her. 'I deliberately misled you. I knew you thought I was Jan, and I
let you go on thinking so because I didn't want you to go
after her. But my handbag was in the bedroom with my
passport in it. That will convince you that I'm speaking the
truth.'

He paused, and for a moment she thought it was to consider what she had said. But it was only to remove his
stained velvet jacket and toss it over the back of a con-
venient chair. His tie followed it, and he began to unfasten

his shirt, his mocking eyes observing her sudden pallor and the unsteadiness of her breathing.

'And I suppose I am to rush off to Rome immediately to check on this—fabrication?' He shook his head as he tossed his shirt to the floor. 'I'm sorry, *bella mia*, I have—better things to do. Now stop cowering there like a frightened nymph, and come to me,' he added with a touch of impatience. 'It's what we both want, so why pretend?'

He held out his arms imperatively, his brows drawing together in a deepening frown when she made not the slightest attempt to move.

'Don't make me fetch you, *cara*,' he spoke almost lightly, but the underlying threat was unmistakable.

'You've got to believe me,' Juliet said desperately. 'I am not my sister. Surely you must have seen photographs of her in magazines? And that—party you mentioned. You saw her in person there.'

'Very much so,' he commented derisively, his tone bringing the colour flooding back to her face. 'But your own common sense must tell you, Janina, that when you dance for a man wearing nothing but one small triangle of lace, he is unlikely to be studying your face. As for magazine photographs'—he shrugged—'once the make-up artists have done their work, you could be anyone. No, you don't convince me, *cara*, and my tolerance of these maidenly shrinkings is decreasing by the minute.' His eyes went over her, and she shrank back against the sofa, terrified at the frankly sensual appraisal she saw in them. She heard him laugh softly.

'Give yourself, *cara*,' he said almost gently. 'Don't make me take you.'

'Santino—please!' Frustrated, helpless tears were welling up in her eyes. 'Don't—don't do something we will both regret ...'

He smiled. 'You mean that I'll hate myself in the morn-

ing? How very old-fashioned—and also untrue. I shan't
hate myself, my lovely one, and you won't hate me either.'

Without haste he cancelled the remaining distance between them and drew her shivering body against the
warmth of his. With casual mastery he detached the folds
of the dress she was still clutching from her shaking hands
and let it fall to the ground. For a long moment he looked
at her, and then with an indrawn breath he slid to his knees
beside her, pressing his face against the satin-smooth skin
of her stomach.

'Call yourself Juliet if you wish, *carissima*,' he whispered,
as his lips plundered a trail of kisses across her body. 'Tonight, such a name for you will not be inappropriate.'

A little moan that she could not suppress rose in her
throat. In spite of herself, his hands and mouth on her body
were arousing desires and emotions that she could not hope
to deny. Even his lightest touch was enough to set slow
fires burning all over her, and her brain refused to work
coherently as his slow, lingering, utterly expert caresses reduced her into compliance.

Somewhere deep inside her, a little voice was crying out
in agony that she wanted to be his—yes—but for her own
sake, not because he had mistaken her for Jan. But then his
fingers, exploring the smooth curve of her slender hips, slid
downwards with new urgency to rid her of her last remaining scrap of clothing and even that small voice was mute,
silenced by the tide of totally mindless longing which en-
gulfed her.

Somewhere in the distance, in another lifetime perhaps,
she could hear a strange noise—far-off thunder, maybe, or
even the pounding of her own heart. It didn't really matter
very much as her arms slid up past his shoulders to wind
round his neck and she waited for the moment when he
would lift her in his arms and carry her up to that big
shuttered room upstairs with the wide bed.

But the pounding noise was still there, and there were voices now intermingled with it, and she heard Santino curse swiftly and coldly before he put her from him none too gently.

He picked up her crumpled dress and tossed it to her. 'Cover yourself, *cara*,' he ordered as he found his shirt and thrust his arms into it. 'It seems we have visitors.'

For one dazed, incredulous moment she stared at him before sanity returned, and the devastating realisation of what he had said. With a little gasp of shame and panic, she huddled into her clothes, fumbling for the long zip on the dress with hands that would scarcely obey her, her face crimson as she realised the exact extent of her self-betrayal.

He was already at the door, turning half-impatiently to make sure she was ready before he drew back the heavy iron bolts which fastened it. She found the scarf for her hair, but she was trembling too much to replace it, and she sank down on the nearest sofa, winding it round her shaking fingers.

'Santino!' It was a woman's voice, and Juliet flinched involuntarily as it came to her ears. Was she to be spared nothing? she wondered.

But the woman who erupted into the room only a second later was certainly not of an age to have been Santino's mistress. Her black hair was liberally streaked with grey, and her figure though not without dignity was short and inclined to be plump. She was elegantly dressed in black and diamonds glinted on her fingers and in her ears, and it only needed Santino's amazed 'Mamma?' to make her identity more than clear.

A flood of excited Italian burst upon Juliet's ears as she sat on the corner of her sofa, wishing that the floor would open and swallow her. But there was no chance that she could make her escape to the stairs unobserved. In spite of her impassioned monologue which Santino was listening to as if he had been turned to stone, the little lady's eyes were darting all over the room and they had already sharpened as Juliet came under their scrutiny. She had also been seen by the man who had accompanied her into the room, a tall man with a calm rather distinguished face and iron-grey hair who was staring at her with a puzzled frown as if she reminded him of someone.

Juliet bit her lip. She knew what he must be thinking, and she did not even have the saving grace of a denial. But for their arrival, Santino would be making love to her at that moment.

Even as she acknowledged silently the truth of this realisation, she heard Santino say impatiently, '*Si, Mamma, ma un momento. Aspetti, per piacere.*'

He turned away abruptly and came over to where she was sitting.

His dark face was harsh as he looked down at her. 'Mario is in hospital,' he said. 'He was injured when his car crashed near Naples.'

Her lips parted as she registered what he was saying, and an anxious gasp escaped her. 'Jan,' she got out. 'Was Jan with him? Is she all right?'

His mouth curled contemptuously. 'Is that all you can say?' he demanded. 'More lies, more fairy tales?'

Before she could reply, the Signora walked across the room and stood staring at her. '*Chi e lei?*' she demanded curiously.

'Speak English, Mamma,' Santino advised. 'It's the only thing Signorina Laurence understands.'

'Laur-ence?' The Signora pronounced the name thoughtfully, then recoiled. '*Santa Madre*, it is the name of that one!' She swung on Santino. 'What you do with a girl who has the same name as that one?'

'Mamma,' Santino took her arm pacifically, 'this is the

girl that Mario was involved with, but you don't have to worry any more because ...'

'This girl?' The Signora gazed long and hard at Juliet, her eyes narrowed. 'No,' she said at last. 'Is like. Is very like. But is not that girl.'

'Mamma, what are you saying?' Santino's voice was hoarse.

'I say is not that girl,' his mother replied reasonably. 'How she come here, anyway, when she in hospital, same as my Mario?'

Santino paid no attention to the serene logic of her argument. He said half to himself, 'But it can't be!' Then he took Juliet's arms in a grip that hurt and drew her to her feet. He said harshly, 'Who are you, and this time it had better be the truth.'

Juliet flung back her head defiantly. 'I told you who I was,' she said. 'My name is Juliet and I'm Janina Laurence's older sister. I'm a schoolteacher and I come from England.'

'A schoolteacher?' he echoed with a mirthless laugh. He released her and turned away. '*Dio*, what a mess!'

The Signora laid a beautifully manicured hand on his arm. 'What does she say? That she is the sister of that other one—that ...'

'*Sì*, Mamma,' Santino hastily cut across the clearly uncomplimentary description his mother was about to give. 'She is her sister.'

'Holy Saints!' The Signora tottered to one of the other sofas and sat down, producing a lacy handkerchief which she pressed to her mouth. 'How I am cursed,' she announced to the room at large. 'Some mothers have sons who marry and give them grandchildren. I have sons who play around with women no one will ever marry. Is it not bad enough that Mario who is young and a fool runs off with such a one? Have you learned no more wisdom than he has?'

She made no further effort to speak English, but broke into a flood of impassioned Italian which Juliet was thankful she did not understand, judging by the fulminating looks the Signora kept casting in her direction. Santino made no attempt to stem the flow of words, but stood quietly his head slightly bent. Juliet saw that he was very white under his tan.

It was the other man who came to the rescue. Strolling forward, he laid a hand on the Signora's shoulder. His English was good but heavily accented. 'Peace, *cara*. Santino understands your feelings. There is no need to continue.' He turned towards Juliet and made her a courteous old-fashioned bow. 'You will forgive my wife, *signorina*. In her anxiety over her son she has neglected to tell you that your sister who you will have heard is also in hospital is not seriously injured. A couple of broken ribs, that is all.'

Juliet gave a long sigh. 'Thank God!' she murmured. 'Thank you, *signore*. I—I shall have to let my mother know.'

'But not tonight,' Santino said brusquely. 'You have heard my stepfather say she is not badly injured.' He looked down at her and his face was that of a forbidding stranger. The lover who had caressed her to the brink of madness and surrender only a few short minutes before had vanished as if he had never existed. Perhaps he never had. He had spoken of fairy tales; maybe it had all been part of it. She felt very weary suddenly and a little sick. She wanted very badly to go to her room, away from these hostile eyes that seemed to be boring into her, but her legs seemed to have turned to jelly and would not support her properly so that she staggered a little as she started to move.

'*Attenzione*, Santino!' It was his stepfather speaking. 'I think the *signorina* is unwell.'

Without a word, and before she could utter a protest, Santino swung her up into his arms and started towards the stairs, his face paler than she had ever seen it and strangely set as if he found his task distasteful.

But had she really expected anything else? she thought, a feeling of desolation creeping over her. She'd known all along what would happen once he knew the truth.

Santino did not speak until they were inside the room she had moved her clothes into. He laid her on the bed and turned away.

'I'll send Annunziata to you,' he said abruptly.

'Santino.' She levered herself up on to one elbow and gazed at him appealingly. 'How did it happen—the accident, I mean?'

'I don't know,' he said levelly. 'It is one of many questions for which answers will have to be found. As soon as I have some definite information, I will let you know. Goodnight——' he paused and his mouth curved slightly into a mirthless smile. 'Goodnight, Giulietta.'

He walked to the door and went out, closing it behind him. Juliet lay back against her pillows, her eyes closed, fighting the tears of strain that threatened to overwhelm her. Poor Jan, she thought, starting her honeymoon in hospital, but she supposed she ought to be glad that they had both apparently escaped serious injury. And she should be glad too that the whole story was out in the open now, and that her charade was over for good and all.

I should be glad, she told herself. I should be—but I'm not.

She turned over and buried her face in the pillow.

'If only they'd waited a few more hours,' she whispered achingly. 'Oh, why did they have to come just at that moment? Why couldn't they have let me have tonight?'

Juliet awoke very early the next morning. She had not expected to be able to sleep, but a rather worried-looking Annunziata had appeared at her bedside the previous night carrying a tray with a glass beaker in a silver holder which she told Juliet contained a *tisana*. It was hot and tasted of herbs, but it was oddly refreshing and under Annunziata's watchful gaze Juliet felt impelled to drain it down to the last drop. Almost in spite of herself, she felt soothed, and it was soothing too to feel Annunziata's hands smoothing her pillow and drawing the coverlet up around her shoulders with little pats and soft mutterings.

Although none of her problems had actually retreated during the night, Juliet could not help but feel refreshed by her hours of deep, dreamless sleep. She got out of bed and wandered across to the window, pushing back the heavy shutters. Below her the sea moved gently, every tiny billow sparkling gold in the early sun. The air smelt fresh and clean, and a solitary bird wheeled and dipped high above in the cloudless sky.

Juliet sighed and pushed her hair back from her face. Somehow today she had to get to the hospital to see Jan. Although she wasn't seriously hurt, broken ribs were nevertheless uncomfortable, and she would obviously be shaken after the crash.

At the same time Juliet had to face the fact that she was not looking forward to this reunion with her sister. She felt that her discoveries of the past few days had transformed her into a stranger—someone in fact whom she would have preferred in other circumstances to keep at arm's length.

Hypocrite, she told herself fiercely, as she turned away from the window and picked up her robe and toilet bag. What point was there in priding yourself on your virtue, if you had never been tempted? And Juliet now knew only too well how fatally easy it was to succumb to temptation once it was offered.

But for the arrival of his mother and stepfather, she would have awoken this morning in Santino's arms to heaven knows what regrets and recriminations.

Lost in her troublous thoughts, she wandered out on to the gallery and almost collided with a figure leaving the bathroom.

'Oh, *scusi*.' She looked up startled, expecting to see the Signora, but this was a woman she had never seen before, slightly younger than the Signora but with the same cosseted well-groomed appearance, and wearing an expensive negligee.

The woman did not reply to her hasty apology, but stood looking Juliet over in silence, a half-smile curving her lips. But it wasn't a friendly or a pleasant smile, the sort normally exchanged by house guests in early morning encounters on the way to the bathroom. It was all too knowing, and bore more than a trace of malice, and Juliet felt defiant colour begin to rise in her cheeks as she suffered this close scrutiny.

At last the woman moved away, taking a last searching look at Juliet as she did so, her eyes lingering particularly on her hair. As she passed with a whisper of silk, a cloud of exquisite perfume hung on the air.

The same perfume gave the bathroom a more than usually exotic atmosphere and Juliet did not linger over her bathing and dressing. She felt uneasy, and knew that it was because of that encounter on the gallery. She wondered who the glamorous stranger might be, and when she had arrived on the scene.

She put on a pair of denim jeans and a sleeveless vest in a black silky material and went downstairs. The *salotto* was deserted except for Annunziata who was laying places for breakfast in the dining alcove. She beamed expansively when she saw Juliet, and seizing her arm led her to the great door with its massive iron studs which stood open this morning to admit the faint breeze. Juliet supposed with some amusement that she was being sent for an early morning stroll to give an edge to her appetite, but she soon realised her mistake. Annunziata was chattering away and gesturing towards the shore. Looking down, Juliet saw a dark figure standing motionless at the water's edge and realised with a painful thump of her heart that it was Santino. Her impulse was to run back indoors and take refuge in her room, but that would only be delaying the inevitable. Sooner or later she would have to speak to him, to ask him to help her get to Naples. She had no choice as her own money and traveller's cheques were presumably still in Jan's apartment in Rome.

Slowly she started down the steps, her hands instinctively balling into fists at her sides as she moved, her nails digging painfully into the palms as she struggled to maintain her composure.

She wished she could have emulated his own soundless approach of the previous day, but of course, he heard her and half-turned frowningly to see who was coming to disturb his reverie. His frown did not lift when he saw her, and she felt absurdly hurt. It took an immense effort of will to keep walking, slithering and sliding over the stones until she reached his side.

'*Buon giorno,*' he said quietly.

He was wearing faded jeans, and an old blue shirt open almost to the waist. A strong line of stubble along his jaw indicated that he had not bothered to shave that morning, but neither this nor his faintly bloodshot eyes and heavy scowl could detract in the least from his sheer virile appeal and Juliet felt her stomach contract painfully as she looked at him. Afraid that those penetrating tawny eyes would read her thoughts, she hurried into speech.

'*Signore,* I—I need your help . . .'

'And I need yours,' he interrupted flatly.

'Mine?' She stared at him, totally at a loss.

'You seem surprised.' He smiled without amusement. 'Did it never occur to you when you embarked on this madness that there would be repercussions?'

'Yes—no—oh, I don't know,' she said wretchedly. 'It didn't seem important at the time. All that mattered was that Jan should marry your brother if that was what she wanted.'

He looked at her broodingly. 'It is so important that this little sister should have her own way in everything?'

'No.' Juliet swallowed. 'Although I suppose she is—rather spoiled. She's so lovely, it's hard to say no to her,' she added defensively, seeing his mouth curl cynically. 'She's always been so loved, so admired all her life that perhaps she's—let everything get out of proportion.'

'Your loyalty far outweighs your common sense, *cara*,' he commented with a derisive smile. 'What you are saying is that to satisfy the whim of a spoiled, selfish little bitch, other lives must be thrown in chaos.'

'But it wasn't just a whim,' she protested. 'Mario had to marry her, don't you see ...' Her voice tailed away when she saw the way he was looking at her.

'*Santa Maria*,' he said very quietly. 'Is this something new? Something that you have not told me, that even my mother has not heard? Speak the truth!'

Juliet bowed her head miserably. 'Jan is going to have Mario's baby,' she admitted in a low voice.

His face darkened furiously, and he turned away cursing under his breath. There was a long silence.

'So there is to be a child,' he said at last, his back turned to her. 'When?'

'I don't know that,' she said. 'I wasn't meant to know.' Quickly she explained her reasons for visiting Jan. 'When she told me about the baby, I could quite understand why she wanted to get married as quickly and quietly as possible,' she continued. 'That's why I decided to help her. Mim—my mother—has always been so proud of Jan—she's the success story of the family. It would break her heart if Jan were to have an illegitimate child.'

He muttered something under his breath. 'I suppose there is a certain irony in the situation,' he said after a moment or two. 'You working to achieve this marriage to spare your mother's feelings, and I working against it for the same reason. I was not of course aware that you or your mother existed. According to the story your sister told Mario, she was an orphan brought up in foster-homes without a living relative.'

'Oh, no!' The appalled words broke from Juliet's throat. 'She—she couldn't have said such a thing!'

He smiled a little. 'To achieve her desires, I think she could probably say anything. You are sure, are you, that this baby exists and is not yet another figment of her imagination?'

'I'm sure she's pregnant,' she admitted unhappily. 'She—she'd put on weight, and she was very ill that first morning.'

'Hm.' He paused, then said coldly and brutally, 'So she decided to foist the paternity of her bastard on to Mario.'

Juliet's eyes filled with tears. 'That's a despicable thing to say!'

'It may also be the truth,' he said. 'Not that I imagine she would ever admit it, even if she knew what the truth was.'

'You shouldn't say these things,' she whispered, her lips trembling. 'You don't know her.'

'No, but I thought I did,' he answered abruptly. 'Instead, I knew you, *cara*, and last night that knowledge was almost complete.'

Juliet felt her throat tighten. The silence between them seemed to stretch on forever, and become almost tangible. Oh God, she found herself thinking, don't let him move, don't let him touch me. The slightest physical contact between them and she had the oddest sensation that she would shiver into a thousand tiny fragments.

'Please don't let's talk about—last night,' she said at last, haltingly.

'Of course not,' he agreed too urbanely. 'Let us dismiss it from our minds—pretend that it never happened.'

Staring down at the pebbles at her feet, she said slowly 'After all, it isn't as if it—meant anything. You—you thought I was Jan, that's all, which is what I wanted you to think, so it was my own fault ...' Her voice tailed away rather desperately and there was nothing on earth that could have forced her to look up and meet his gaze.

'Very true.' His voice was silky. 'You are an accomplished actress, *mia cara*—almost too accomplished for your own good, if you will forgive me for saying so. If you intend to make impersonations of your sister part of your way of life, I advise you to choose your company rather carefully. Next time you may not get off quite so lightly.'

A voice inside her was screaming, 'But I didn't get off lightly! Not lightly at all.' And for a moment she was terrified that she had spoken aloud, and betrayed to him all her misery and regret and hopeless longing.

'Jan can manage without my help from now on,' she said with a surface lightness she was far from feeling. 'She has a husband to look after her now and ...'

'It seems not.' His tone was dry. 'I'm afraid your dangerous pretence was all in vain, Giulietta. Mario and your sister are not married, nor ever likely to be, according to my mother's information.'

'But they must be!' Juliet burst out wildly. 'It can't all have been for nothing—it can't!'

She sank down on the nearest rock and buried her face in her hands. It was impossible that she'd let her whole life be turned upside down, relinquished her peace of mind and much of her self-respect, possibly for ever, only to be casually told that it had all been in vain.

At last, with a long quivering sigh, she looked up and met his eyes.

'So you've won—after all.'

'It isn't a victory I'm particularly proud of,' he said harshly. 'And it isn't complete by any means.'

She made the effort to get to her feet. 'The favour I wanted to ask,' she said wearily. 'Can you have me taken to Naples to see Jan? She'll be upset. She'll need someone.'

'At the moment she is in good hands,' he said. 'Yet I can understand your anxiety. My mother also fears some calamity will happen if she does not visit Mario immediately. But there is a problem.'

She looked at him, startled, and he gave a little twisted smile.

'I did tell you that I needed your help,' he reminded her. 'When my mother received the message from the hospital, she was spending a few days in a villa at Brindisi with my stepfather's sister. When they set off to come to me here, she insisted on accompanying them—for reasons best known to herself.' He paused. 'When they arrived, I had no idea they were not alone, and I was frankly horrified when Mamma revealed that Vittoria was waiting in the car. She is clearly determined to accompany us to Naples later this morning, and there is no way of preventing her without arousing her suspicions still further.'

'But why should you wish to prevent her?'

Santino thrust his hands into his pockets irritably. 'Because she is not only my mother's sister-in-law,' he said with an edge to his voice, 'she is also the *madrina*—the godmother—to Mario's fiancée Francesca.'

'Mario's—fiancée?' The breath left Juliet's body in a disbelieving gasp.

He smiled thinly. 'You didn't know he was already *fidanzato*? Your sister had left that small detail out of her marriage plans?'

'She mentioned something—about an arranged marriage.' Juliet bent her head. 'But I got the impression that it was all in the future—nothing definite.'

He raised his eyebrows. 'The date of the ceremony had already been fixed,' he drawled. 'Francesca naturally knows nothing about your sister's existence. She is young, very lovely, very innocent, and she loves my headstrong fool of a brother more than he deserves. Naturally, we do not wish her to know how churlishly he has repaid her devotion.'

'No,' Juliet agreed dully. 'But what has this got to do with her godmother? Surely she wouldn't ...?'

'You think not?' Santino shook his head. 'When Vittoria's husband died he did not leave her as well provided for as she believed he would—or should, though she is far from poor, you understand. Francesca's family on the other hand is very wealthy, and Francesca herself is a considerable heiress—and Vittoria has a son, one year younger than Mario. If she could destroy the engagement between Mario and Francesca, then perhaps ...' He paused significantly.

'But that would be wicked,' Juliet said incredulously. 'To deliberately set out to ruin someone's happiness for monetary gain ...' She caught his ironic glance and her voice tailed into silence, while a blush rose to the roots of her hair.

'Wicked, yes,' he said drily. 'But to Vittoria's mind, eminently practical. She already suspects that Mario has been—playing around. If she arrives at the clinic and finds your sister in an adjoining room, injured in the same crash, it will not take her long to supply the rest of the details.'

'So how are you going to stop her?' Juliet spread her hands out helplessly.

'I am going to create a smokescreen,' he said. 'With your help. She knows your sister well, of course, but you she does not know, although she will have little difficulty in detecting the resemblance when you do meet.'

'I think we met outside the bathroom earlier,' Juliet confessed.

He shrugged. 'It doesn't matter. All you have to do when

we return to the *castello* for breakfast is to accept without comment the story I shall tell her to explain your presence, and also Janina's presence in the clinic in Naples.'

'What are you going to say?' Juliet felt slightly sick.

'That you and I are engaged to be married,' he said blandly.

'*What?*' She almost shrieked the word. 'You're mad!'

'No.' He shook his head. 'Listen to me, *cara*, and don't be hysterical. By now Vittoria will have seen the newspapers and know there has been some muddle because I am not here with Janina, I am here with you. She enjoys scandal and has a nose for gossip. In fact she is not above selling stories about some of her dearest friends to newspaper columnists, not merely here in Italy but abroad as well. Well, I can explain away that particular story—a reporter was too hasty and made a mistake. Two sisters, both red-haired, both English and beautiful—a simple error in identities. So today, I announce that we are going to be married, and that I had already set the wheels of a family party in action by inviting Mario down here and requesting him to bring your sister with him. Before I could issue invitations to the rest of the family—including Francesca—Mario's car was involved in that unfortunate incident.'

'I won't do it!' Juliet's hands clenched into fists at her sides, the knuckles showing white.

'Your help in exchange for mine—that was the deal,' he reminded her.

'But you can't bargain like that,' she protested.

'Why not?' The tawny eyes were fixed compellingly on her face. 'You are an accomplished actress, *mia*, as I told you. All you have to do is act the part of my loving fiancée for a few days—and persuade your sister to co-operate in our story.'

'I—persuade Jan?' Juliet shook her head. 'You have to be joking!'

'Oh, I was never more serious, *cara*,' he said softly. 'Consider, if you will. At the moment, the only hint of scandal surrounding this unsavoury affair is the story I myself fed to the newspapers, which our engagement will give the lie to. But what will happen if the true facts emerge, eh? Publicity will be unavoidable—Vittoria will see to that—and it won't be simply in a few Italian newspapers. She will make sure the story makes the headlines in London and New York as well. It can only be a matter of time before your mother whose feelings you are so anxious to spare sees it. You cannot pretend it would add to her happiness or well-being to read such things.'

There was a long, appalled silence while Juliet frantically attempted to collect her thoughts. She remembered the malice in the eyes of the woman she had seen that morning and imagined that malice translated into newspaper terms and pictures. It was a degrading and frightening prospect, and a blow from which Mrs Laurence might never recover.

'One last point,' Santino said gently but inexorably. 'You may not know, but Vittoria is the Contessa Leontana at whose party your sister once disrobed with such spectacular success. I cannot imagine she would leave out such a juicy incident if she decided—regretfully, of course—to tell what she knew to the gutter press.'

'But there must be some other way,' Juliet said desperately. 'I—I can't pretend to be engaged to you—you must see that.'

His brows drew together haughtily. 'I regret that I see nothing of the kind. The engagement I propose is largely for your own sake, although considering the trick you played on me, I owe you nothing. Once you are safely established as my *fidanzata*, Vittoria will not dare snipe at you, because you will be under the protection of my family, of which her own brother is a member. Even she would hesitate to make trouble under such circumstances.'

Juliet looked away at the sun-drenched horizon and found it blurred by the tears that were threatening to overwhelm her.

'And your mother?' she asked as soon as she thought she had sufficient control over her voice. 'She has no very high opinion of either my sister or myself, from what I gathered last night. How will she accept this pseudo-engagement, or do you mean to tell her that it's only a fraud?'

'That, *cara*, will remain a secret, just between the two of us,' he drawled. 'You will oblige me by not even confiding in your sister. As for my mother, there is no need for you to concern yourself. I will deal with her.'

'And how long has this—farce to go on for?' she demanded bitterly.

'Until Mario and Francesca are safely married—or until I decide to call a halt,' he said very softly. 'Whichever is the sooner. Don't look so anguished, Giulietta. Our betrothal will be conducted in public only. I shan't force my attentions on you in private.' He took her chin in his hand and studied her face almost reflectively. 'Are you a virgin?'

She could have reacted in a number of ways to such a question, from old-fashioned outrage to a defiant reminder of the fact that it was none of his business. Instead, her face burning under his scrutiny, she heard herself mutter, 'Yes—does it matter?'

'I think it does.' He released her chin. 'I may not have been kind to you, Giulietta, but at least I don't have to live with the knowledge that I seduced you.' He smiled rather mirthlessly. 'In Italy, a girl's purity before marriage is still highly prized. I am glad I did not cheat your husband, *mia cara*.'

He waited for a moment, but she did not reply, then reached forward and took her unresisting hand.

'Come,' he said. 'Let us go back now and tell them our —joyous news.'

And as Juliet followed him across the rocks to the road and the steps up to the *castello*, she realised for the first time in her life that sometimes the most painful tears of all are those that one cannot afford to shed.

CHAPTER SEVEN

'WELL, darling, you have been clever.' Jan leaned back against her pillows and stared up at her sister, her eyes glittering. 'I never knew you were quite such a fast worker —and Santino Vallone is the cherry off a very big cake.'

Juliet felt her already guilty flush deepen at her sister's mocking words.

'Let's not discuss that now,' she said hurriedly. 'How— how are you, Jan?'

'As well as can be expected—isn't that the phrase they use?' Jan petulantly hoisted one of her pillows, and winced at the resulting pain the hasty movement had caused to her injured ribs. 'The infant is still firmly in place, just in case you were hoping I'd have a convenient miscarriage.'

'Oh, Jan!' Juliet sank limply down on to the chair at the side of the bed. 'What an appalling thing to say!'

'Have you told your handsome betrothed that his first nephew—or niece, of course—is going to be a bastard?' Jan demanded maliciously, and laughed. 'I wonder if he'll invite me to the wedding. Only if it's as whirlwind as the courtship, I suppose.' She looked her sister up and down. 'Darling Julie,' she said without a trace of affection in her tone. 'Always so sane and sensible, like lace-up shoes. Has the gorgeous Santino managed to unlace you, or have you convinced him that vestal virgins are the in thing this year?' She gave a little giggle. 'Poor Santino! It must be a new thing in his experience, finding a girl who doesn't sleep around. I hope the novelty lasts, sweetie. How awful to have your husband die of boredom on your wedding night!'

'Awful indeed,' Juliet returned pleasantly. 'But just think what a wealthy widow I'll be.'

Jan raised her eyebrows. 'Touché,' she remarked appreciatively. 'The kitten is developing claws at last. If this is what a couple of days with Santino can do, there may be hope for you yet.'

Juliet looked down at her hands, clasped in her lap. 'Jan,' she said quietly, 'what went wrong—with you and Mario, I mean?'

Jan gave an irritable lift of a shoulder. 'Let's just say that his family arguments began to weigh more heavily with him than mine, and leave it at that, shall we?'

'It wouldn't have had anything to do with the fact that he was engaged already?'

Jan's faint scowl deepened perceptibly. 'So your involvement with Santino has also included a crash course in family relationships,' she said. 'Yes, of course I knew about Francesca.'

'And that didn't stop you?' Juliet stared down at her sister in utter perplexity. 'You knew he belonged to someone else, and yet . . .'

'If you're going to sit around moralising at me, then you can go.' Jan glared at her openly. 'I took a gamble which didn't come off, that's all. Anyway, I can't imagine why the boring little Francesca didn't stay in her convent for life. That would have solved everyone's problem.'

'Are you so sure?' Juliet asked with some bitterness. 'From what I've been able to gather in the past couple of days you haven't exactly presented yourself as the ideal bride.'

'Perhaps not,' Jan said coolly. 'But then I never pretended to opt for the role of the family virgin. That's yours, my sweet, and I can only say you're welcome to it.'

A troubled silence fell in the small sunny room on the

fourth floor of the clinic. Juliet began to feel as if she was living through an endless nightmare. She had told herself so often that everything that had happened to her, even the foolish deception she had practised would be worth it if Jan and Mario were married. She had believed with a kind of silly romanticism that they were a pair of star-crossed lovers whom she was helping on their way to happiness. Now it was more than evident that this was far from being the case. Jan seemed put out at the upset to her plans, but little more. Juliet doubted whether she had any genuine feeling for Mario at all.

Muted sounds of traffic drifted up from the street below, underlying the reality of the situation. This was no dream, and nor was the heavy emerald she wore on her engagement finger, the type of flawless gem she had never imagined she would ever possess. Not, of course, that she did possess it, she reminded herself hastily. It was a loan—a stage property. If she had found the role of Jan difficult to play, then the part of Santino's fiancée was doubly hard, for she had to act like a loving woman, yet at the same time conceal the fact that no acting ability was needed. She loved him, yet she could acknowledge the painful truth only to herself. He must not know, he must never know, she'd kept repeating to herself over and over again, like a charm, as they had driven to the clinic, the Signora silent and watchful in the seat behind.

Sitting beside him, watching him drive, had not been easy. She'd wanted very badly to touch him, to have the right to put her hand over his, however fleetingly, even to let her arm brush his casually. But she didn't dare, because she knew that any such gesture, no matter how carefully masked, would give her away instantly. Any physical contact with him was still too new, too raw to be casual.

Neither of them had said a great deal, probably because everything that was needful had been said already, she thought dully. Santino had briefed her fully in the short time he was alone with her to give her the ring. He had also outlined the explanation he intended to give to his family of their sudden engagement.

Although she had been prepared, it was still a shock to hear this coldly enunciated by the Signora.

'My son tells me he has done you a great wrong, *signorina*, and that his honour and yours demands he make reparation by marrying you.' She gave a glacial shrug. 'So be it.'

His stepfather had murmured something in an embarrassed voice, patting her shoulder rather clumsily. It was obvious he had little idea what to make of the situation.

But when the Contessa Leontana came down to the *salotto*, smiling lazily, darting malicious glances under her lashes, Juliet saw for the first time what family solidarity could mean. Santino had announced to his mother that she was his chosen bride. *Bene*. No outsider would be allowed to see how poorly she thought of his choice or the motives of honour which had prompted it. Juliet found herself presented to the Contessa by an almost vivacious Signora, who was not above inventing a few additional details to add verisimilitude to the story.

Juliet heard to her amazement that she had met Santino in London the previous year, and that they would have been married then only they had agreed to test their feelings by a year's separation. And yes, it was quite true that she was the sister of the lovely Janina who modelled for Di Lorenzo. Such a mercy that her looks had apparently been spared in the accident, otherwise what a tragic ending it would have been to her happy journey to celebrate her sister's *fidanzamento*. And Mario too, who had offered to drive her down. God was indeed merciful that he had been spared serious injury.

The Contessa was all smiles and congratulations when

she turned to Juliet, but there was a blank look in her eyes
which stated quite plainly that she was not altogether im-
pressed with what she had been told. Juliet was relieved to
find that the Contessa's knowledge of English was even
scantier than the Signora's, which meant that she could
avoid any overt questioning.

The Contessa tried hard to be a passenger in Santino's
car for the drive to the clinic, but she was firmly put aside
by the smiling Signora, who declared she wished to become
better acquainted with her daugher-in-law to be. It was with
evident ill-grace that the Contessa accepted a seat in her
brother's car.

But it was just as well, Juliet told herself a number of
times on the journey. She doubted whether the illusion of
the happy family party could have been sustained in the
presence of a third party. As it was, no one had to make
polite conversation or trouble the tense silence that pre-
vailed in the car for most of the hot and dusty journey.
When the Signora did speak it was to direct terse questions
at Santino. The tone in which these were uttered and his
tight-lipped replies left Juliet in little doubt as to the subject, and she felt herself cringe unhappily inside. She
wished that she was a thousand miles away, or better still
that she had never succumbed to the temptation of coming
to Italy at all. Look where her well-meaning interference
had led her, she thought miserably, to heartbreak. And yet,
paradoxically, she knew she could not honestly say she regretted her meeting with Santino. Until that moment she
had been only half alive, although she hadn't realised it. But
she knew it now, and she knew too that having caught even a
brief glimpse of the sheer radiance that life could bring, she
would never again be content to settle for second-best.

On arrival at the clinic, a large modern building in ex-
tensive grounds on the outskirts of the city, they had been
met by a smiling nun, one of the nursing order who ran the

clinic, whose reassuring words brought a smile of relief to the Signora's strained face.

Santino had turned to Juliet. 'I shall take my mother to see Mario,' he said abruptly. 'I imagine you would prefer to see your sister alone for a while.'

She murmured her assent, but now she was beginning to regret that she had not waited to confront Jan until he was free to accompany her. At least the foregoing painful little scene might have been avoided in the presence of a third party—especially an intimidating presence like Santino's.

'What's the matter?' Jan's voice broke across her reverie. 'Love's sweet dream turning sour already? That's the trouble with whirlwind romances, of course. It's very exciting while you're actually being swept along, but you tend to come back down to earth with a bump eventually.'

'It isn't that.' Juliet got up restlessly and walked over to the window, her fingers playing with the blind cord as she stood looking out. 'I—I have to know what you intend to do next.'

'You mean will I go along with this farrago of nonsense that you and Santino have dreamed up to explain why Mario and I just happened to be in the same car together miles from Rome?' Jan gave a little mirthless laugh. 'Can you give me one good reason why I should? After all, I owe the Vallone clan nothing—but nothing.'

'Would it be an added incentive if I were to say that Vittoria Leontana will be here any moment, and that if she discovers the true facts you can forget any hopes you may have had about keeping this whole miserable business from Mim?' Juliet kept her voice level with an effort.

'Vittoria?' Jan said sharply. 'What the hell is she doing here? She's the last person I ever want to see again—spiteful, conniving bitch!'

'We won't argue about that,' Juliet said a little wearily. 'It's a little complicated to explain, but she happens to be related by marriage to the Vallone family, and she's travelling to the clinic with Santino's stepfather. In fact they've probably arrived by now.'

Tersely she told her sister all Santino had had to say about the Contessa's nose for scandal, and her contacts in the newspaper world.

'She wouldn't hesitate to make money out of this story,' she ended. 'And can you imagine the effect it will have on Mim if she picks up the newspaper one morning and sees all the details laid out for public inspection?'

She was glad to see that even Jan looked discomposed.

'Of course I can imagine,' she said shortly. 'Very well, sister dear. It seems I'll have to go along with this silly story of yours. But on one condition.'

Juliet's heart sank. 'I'm not sure that I can . . .' she began.

'Then forget it.' Jan waved. 'I'll just have to risk that I can find some way of closing Vittoria's mouth. I know a few details about her that she might not want making public and . . .'

'Oh, no!' Juliet broke in swiftly, sickened. 'For heaven's sake don't bring yourself down to her level. Tell me the condition and—and I'll find some way of fulfilling it.'

Jan leaned back against her pillows. She was smiling again, a small dulcet smile as she looked up at her sister under her eyelashes.

'It's suddenly occurred to me that I need somewhere to go,' she said with a pretty plaintiveness. 'I want to steer clear of Rome for a little while for obvious reasons, and I can't go back to England either, so I need a refuge.' She paused expectantly, looking up at Juliet.

'You mean—you want me to give you a home?' Juliet asked helplessly. 'But, Jan, that's impossible. I have no work permit, for one thing, and no money, or very little. And I have to get back to England before September anyway for the start of term, so . . .'

Jan stared up at her, her eyes narrowing. 'What in the world are you talking about?' she asked impatiently. 'Sometimes, Julie, I think you must be half-witted. I'm not proposing we should shack up together in some hovel to hide my shame, if that's what you were thinking. In case you'd forgotten, you're engaged to marry a very rich man, and I can't imagine that he'll happily accept the idea of your returning to England to teach a crowd of scruffy kids when you could be settling down to raise his own *bambinos*.' She stretched smilingly. 'You've been staying at the *castello*, and presumably that's where you'll be returning when this little errand of mercy is at an end, so I'll come too. I can't wait to get out of this hole,' she added petulantly. 'These nuns are giving me the creeps. I swear they know I'm pregnant.'

'They probably do,' Juliet responded mechanically. 'They are nurses, after all.' Her heart was thudding in sheer horror. She had never imagined that Jan would make such a demand. In fact, she had been sure that she would never want to see any of the Vallones again. Desperately she remembered Santino's stricture that she should not tell her sister that their engagement was a fraud. Yet how could she hope to maintain the illusion even for a week or two if Jan moved in with them?

Besides, in spite of what Santino had said about continuing with the pretence until Mario and Francesca were married, she had hoped to persuade him to let her return to England. She had never intended for one moment to return to the *castello* under any circumstances. Santino might have said that he did not intend to force his attentions on her, but his resolve might falter in the intimate surroundings of the *castello*. And if he did make love to her, she would not be able to hide her response, her deep need any longer, although in some ways, it would be even worse if he stuck to his word and did not touch her, she thought wretchedly.

'Well, what's the matter? You look as if you've seen a ghost,' Jan said. She smiled. 'Come on, love, don't look so stricken. If you were planning a premature honeymoon, I'll be very discreet. I won't intrude, I promise. Besides,' she gave a little knowing chuckle, 'you might be quite glad to have me there—to advise you.'

Juliet felt sick. 'No,' she said. 'It—it's quite impossible ...'

A cool voice from the doorway interrupted. 'Forgive me, but what is impossible?'

Santino strolled forward, his eyes travelling from the tense girl standing at the window, to her smiling, relaxed counterpart in the bed. He paused for a moment, his eyes narrowing a little as he surveyed them both.

'An amazing resemblance,' he murmured, half to himself. 'Has no one ever commented on it before?'

'No,' said Jan. Juliet saw her lips pout a little, and knew she would not be delighted at Santino's comment. She was so used to everyone automatically regarding her as the pretty one, and had always tended to be dismissive towards anyone who in the past had seen the resemblance between them. She gave Santino a beguiling smile. 'You're seeing me at a disadvantage, of course, *signore*. My cosmetic case was one of the casualties in the accident.'

'A small loss compared to what might have been,' Santino said quietly. He stood at the bedside and looked down at her for a long moment. 'So we meet at last, Janina. You should not mourn the loss of your cosmetics, you know. Beauty such as yours needs no adornment.'

Juliet felt herself stiffen, recognising the ironic note in his voice and fearful that Jan would hear it too, but her sister took the remark at its face value and laughed up at him.

'I'm sorry we haven't met before, too,' she said provocatively. 'What a pity, now that we have met, that you happen to be engaged to my sister.'

Juliet had to smother a gasp at the blatancy of the remark and turned away to stare blindly down into the street below. She'd had no idea what Santino was going to say to Jan when he'd entered the room, but she hadn't expected him to stand over the bed, holding her hand in his.

'I too would have preferred a meeting under slightly different circumstances,' she heard him say in reply, but there was no irony in his voice this time, merely a kind of appreciative amusement.

That's the sort of remark he's used to, Juliet thought desolately. She's the sort of woman he's used to. A quick, enjoyable affair, with no bones broken on either side when it's over. They're two of a kind.

His voice went on smoothly. 'So what is impossible, Giulietta? You were in the middle of some explanation when I entered.'

She did not turn and look at him. In a wooden little voice she said, 'Jan wants to come back to the *castello* with us. She's tired of the clinic and—and she feels a quiet rest in the sun would do her good.'

'An admirable idea,' he approved. 'Did you imagine there might be some difficulty?'

Still not looking at either of them, Juliet said in the same wooden voice, 'I wasn't sure that we would be returning to the *castello*.' Her hands were gripped in front of her so tightly that her knuckles were white with the strain.

'Naturally we shall be returning there,' he said almost casually. 'And it would be an excellent arrangement for your sister to accompany us. She would make a far more adequate *compagna* over the next few weeks than Annunziata.'

'A chaperone?' Juliet heard Jan giggle. 'Well, it will be novel anyway.'

Feeling slightly dizzy, she turned away from the window, murmuring something about finding one of the sisters and retrieving Jan's case. As she gained the corridor, Santino came after her.

'What's the matter with you?' he demanded, his fingers grasping her arm. 'Where are you running to?'

She faced him. 'Jan will need her things,' she said defensively, trying to free her arm.

He gestured impatiently. 'She will certainly not be allowed to leave the clinic tonight,' he averred incisively. 'Both she and Mario are still under observation. Tomorrow will be soon enough to find what things of hers were salvaged from the car.' He gave her a searching look. 'What is troubling you?'

'I can't go back to the *castello*,' she said desperately. 'Santino, I can't. I—I must go home—back to England. I have responsibilities . . .'

'You have responsibilities here,' he interrupted coldly. 'You involved yourself in this affair of your own will, but you remain here through mine, and we will see this thing through to the bitter end.'

'And is it your—will that Jan should move in with us to the *castello*?' she demanded.

'The idea had not occurred to me before,' he said coolly. 'But it has much to recommend it, particularly as I learn that Francesca and her mother are on their way here to visit Mario. I would prefer in some ways for your sister to be at a safe distance before their arrival, so that Vittoria does not get the chance to plant any of her little poisoned darts.'

'And that is the only reason?' she asked, sick at heart.

'No,' he studied her face for a moment, his own expression hardening, 'I admit frankly that it is not. You are neither a child nor a fool, Giulietta, so you must know why I have agreed to invite her.'

'Yes,' she said almost inaudibly, 'I think I do.'

She heard him draw a little breath, and felt his fingers cup her chin lifting her face towards his. With a sense of panic, she knew that he was going to kiss her, and she tore herself free from his slackened grasp, stepping backwards.

'You promised.' Her voice sounded high and a little strained. 'You said that our engagement would only exist in public.'

He took a half-step towards her, his eyebrows lifting mockingly. 'I can think of few places more public than the corridor of a hospital, with the good Sisters likely to come upon us at any minute,' he observed. 'But don't worry, *cara*. Your precious chastity is safe for the moment. My mother has asked me to bring you to Mario's room, so that you may meet him.'

'What a farce it all is,' she said bitterly. 'Very well, *signore*, I'll go and be presented as your future wife. But you don't have to accompany me. As you said, I'm neither a child nor a fool, and I can—just—manage to find two adjoining rooms in a hospital corridor.'

'There are times, Giulietta,' he said quite pleasantly, 'when I could quite willingly beat you. I should go quickly, if I were you, before my impulse turns to compulsion.'

At the door, she hesitated. Inside, through the thin partition, she could hear the Signora talking with great rapidity, with occasional low-voiced interventions by her husband, and she could guess what the subject of the good lady's diatribe was. For a moment she regretted telling Santino she did not want his company. It wasn't the easiest thing in the world to push open a door and walk into a room where you would only be received on sufferance.

If he was still watching her, she decided, she would swallow her pride and ask him to come with her. She swung towards him and paused, the words dying unuttered on her lips. He wasn't watching her. He wasn't even glancing in

her direction. He was walking with cool purpose back to
Janina's room, and as Juliet stood watching with a kind of
sick incredulity, he reached the door and stepped inside.

The door closed behind him, and she was left standing
alone in a long empty corridor.

As she viewed her luxurious hotel suite that evening, it
occurred to Juliet rather forcibly the kind of influence that
money like Santino's could have, producing accommodation
like this for his family in one of the best hotels at the height
of the tourist season.

Nothing had been forgotten, from the well-stocked re-
frigerated cabinet full of drinks of all kinds to the huge
bowl of red roses placed on the table beside the bed.
Courtesy of the management, she supposed, as she bent
appreciatively to drink in their rich perfume, but she was
wrong. There was a small white card wired to one of the
stems, its surface crossed by the one uncompromising word
'Santino'.

Juliet straightened abruptly and glanced at the signature.
She was strongly tempted to sweep the flowers, bowl and
all, into the wastepaper bin at the other side of the room.
But that would only be an empty gesture, she told herself,
as empty as that which had sent the flowers of love to a girl
masquerading as the beloved. Her most dignified course of
action would be to ignore them altogether, and this would
be far easier if they were not beside her bed.

She picked them up and carried them resolutely out of
the bedroom, into the small elegant sitting room which
opened off it. There was a small gilt-legged table behind the
sofa and she put the bowl down on this, turning it so that
the tell-tale card was concealed.

When a knock fell on the door of the suite just as she
was completing this task, she started so violently that she

jerked the bowl and a few drops of water spilled out on to the marble top of the table.

'Oh, damn!' She scrubbed at it with her handkerchief, remembering belatedly to call '*Avanti*,' and then in the same moment wishing that she had not done so, because it was probably Santino.

But it was the Signora who entered, dressed fashionably in grey lace with the inevitable sparkle of diamonds at her throat and wrists. Juliet gazed at her in some surprise. During the brief visit she had paid to Mario's room, the Signora's manner toward her had been cool and remote, and she had certainly not expected her to seek her company.

The meeting with Mario had been as awkward as she could have imagined. During the rather stilted conversation that followed the introduction, she felt his eyes resting on her wonderingly, and knew resignedly that he too had been struck by her resemblance to Jan. She supposed that he too bore a superficial resemblance to Santino, but it was purely physical. He was good-looking, admittedly, but his face showed his immaturity, and from what she could gather of the ensuing conversation he seemed inclined to blame everyone but himself for what had happened. He was clearly embarrassed to meet Juliet, and his glance at times was speculative, as if he was wondering how much she knew of his affair with her sister, and its result.

She guessed that neither of them was sorry when a nun entered and announced that visiting was at an end for the day. There was no sign of Santino when they emerged, and Santino's stepfather Signor Peretto took it for granted that he would be driving Juliet to the hotel with his wife and the Contessa Leontana, who was waiting downstairs in the foyer.

Since she had arrived at the hotel and been installed in this suite, Juliet had not heard a word from Santino, except for this token offering of roses which he had probably not even chosen himself, she told herself crossly. And now this unexpected visit from his mother. Unconsciously, she squared her shoulders.

'Sit, Giulietta.' The Signora gestured imperiously towards the sofa. 'We talk.'

She waited until Juliet had sat down, then took her place beside her, fixing her keen dark eyes on the younger woman's pale, rather strained face. Juliet bore her scrutiny for a moment or two, then said quietly, 'Was there something you wanted to say to me, *signora*?'

'Plenty things.' The Signora nodded. She gave Juliet a shrewd look. 'You think it strange that I wish to speak to the girl who is to marry my Santino? You are to be *mia nuora*. It is right we should speak. Besides, today I watch you. I watch closely.'

'I had noticed,' Juliet said half under her breath.

'You think that strange too?'

'No—at least, not exactly.' Juliet looked down at her hands clasped in her lap, where Santino's emerald gleamed like green fire. 'I suppose it's natural under the circumstances that you should want to—look me over.' She moistened her lips. 'I—I know you don't like what you see, but ...'

'Is not me that has to like. Is Santino,' the Signora pointed out with some truth. 'Yet you are beautiful. Not as beautiful, it is true, as that other one your sister, but we will not speak of her. She go back to England soon?'

'Not quite yet.' Juliet felt a tight constriction in her throat. 'She—she is coming to stay at the *castello* for a while—to act as a chaperone,' she added.

'To act as *compagna*?' The Signora gave a short laugh. 'Now Santino thinks of that, when it is too late.'

'It's not too late,' Juliet said hurriedly. 'Believe me, *signora*, in England no one marries anyone these days because they've—compromised them. It isn't even as if we—

as if he—I mean—nothing happened between us,' she added rather weakly.

The Signora shrugged. 'Is not important. And this is not England, this is Italy. In Calabria we guard our young girls. Does your father think so little of you that he would not seek revenge on the man who has stolen your honour?'

'My father died some years ago,' Juliet said quietly. 'I admit my mother would be upset, but I was hoping there would be no need for her to know.'

The Signora stared at her. 'Your mother not know?' she enquired on a rising note. 'You not ask her to wedding?'

'Yes, of course.' Juliet felt totally confused. 'It's just that it's not certain there's actually going to be a wedding.'

The Signora gave a brisk nod. 'Is certain,' she said decisively. 'My Santino is a man of honour.' Her face clouded a little. 'My Mario, less so, I fear. But the little Francesca will be good for him.' She nodded again, then surprisingly laid her hand over Juliet's. 'We go down now to dine. You come with us?'

Juliet bit her lip. 'Thank you, but no, *signora*. I have a slight headache. Perhaps I could have some soup sent up on a tray.'

'Soup?' The older woman pulled a face. 'You need food to make you strong, have plenty babies for my Santino.' She gave Juliet an all-encompassing critical look. 'You need colour too. You should eat, and drink red wine.' She waited for a moment then, when she saw that Juliet was adamant, she got to her feet with a faint sigh. 'We speak again, later.'

To Juliet's amazement, she put out a hand and touched her cheek, before turning away towards the door.

After she had gone, Juliet sat motionless for a while, fighting her tears. It was that unexpected gesture of kindness that was making her want to weep, she told herself defensively, not because she was lonely.

She got up and wandered back into the bedroom, notic-

ing in passing how oddly bare the bedside table looked now
without Santino's flowers. A small leather overnight bag,
presumably packed for her by Annunziata, had been placed
on a chair and she unfastened it, extracting a nightdress
and her toilet necessities. The shower cabinet in the bathroom looked more than inviting, she decided. She would
have a shower, and wash her hair at the same time, and
when it was dry she would ring room service and ask them
to bring her some soup.

She had not been entirely untruthful when she had made
the excuse of a headache to the Signora. There was a tension across her scalp and the warm water felt like a benison
as it descended.

She slipped the white lacy nightdress over her still damp
body, and slipped her arms into the matching peignoir,
tying the sash round her slim waist. Winding a towel round
her hair, she walked across to the telephone and lifted the
receiver. The voice at the other end was helpful and she
was soon able to make her wants known, and receive the
promise that her tray would arrive '*subito*'.

Even so she was surprised at how short a space of time
had elapsed before she heard the knock on the outer door of
the suite. Still rubbing her hair with the towel, she walked
across the sitting room and pulled the door open.

But it wasn't a helpful waiter with a supper tray standing
there. It was Santino. His brows rose as he took in her
déshabille, and the damp tendrils of hair hanging on her
shoulders.

'I think we've been here before,' he observed mockingly
as he walked past her into the sitting room. 'Only one thing
is missing.' He pulled one of the crimson roses out of the
bowl, broke off the stem, and tucked the bloom down where
the peignoir parted to reveal the shadowy cleft between her
breasts. 'Remember?' he asked.

'You're so right, I remember,' she jerked out. She threw

the rose down on to the carpet. 'And I can do without the meaningless gestures. If we're playing the memory game, perhaps you might remember you promised not to touch me. Your mother has been telling me *ad nauseam* that you're a man of honour. Well, I don't consider it very honourable to force your way in here and . . .'

'Have you finished?' he interrupted her. His voice was icy with rage and he was very pale under his tan. 'Let us be clear about one thing at least. I did not force my way in here—I knocked and you opened the door to me. *Bene*.'

'I thought you were room service,' she said crossly. 'It was a mistake, and I'd be grateful if you would go.'

His eyes narrowed ominously. 'I'll go when I'm ready, Giulietta. I am here to give you these.' He held out a small bottle containing capsules of some kind. 'From my mother,' he said. 'For the fictitious headache.'

'It isn't fictitious.' She glared at him. 'My head really does ache.'

'You would ache in a great many more places if it were left to me,' he said silkily. 'How dare you refuse my mother's invitation to join our family party downstairs in the restaurant? Acting the part of my fiancée requires you to behave with common courtesy, you know.'

'I don't want to feel any more of a hypocrite than I do already,' she said wearily. She extended her hand and he dropped the bottle of capsules into it.

'Would one small dinner party be such a sacrifice?' His voice was hard.

Yes, her heart cried, when I have to sit opposite you and see you smile at me as if you loved me and know that it all means nothing, absolutely nothing.

She shrugged. 'I think I've made all the sacrifices that can possibly be required of me for one day,' she replied tonelessly. 'I am committed to returning to the *castello*, if you recall, which I didn't expect to have to do.'

'No,' he said between his teeth. 'And this, also, you are not expecting.'

He reached out long arms and pulled her to him hard. The bottle flew out her hand and fell unheeded on to the thick carpet. She managed only to whisper, 'Santino,' achingly, protesting before his hard mouth descended on hers and she was lost, all thought of protest dying under the delight of feeling the passionate demand of his body against hers.

His mouth still locked upon hers, he lifted her up into his arms and carried her into the bedroom, kicking the door shut behind him.

'No!' She tore her mouth away from his. She was suddenly frightened by this new and dark determination she sensed in him. She beat at his chest with her fists. 'No, Santino. Put me down!'

'It will be a pleasure,' he mocked. He dropped her across the bed, then threw himself down beside her, his arm pinning her down almost casually as she struggled to roll away from him.

'Just one more sacrifice, *mia*,' his voice gibed in her ear. Almost insolently he pushed away the concealing folds of the peignoir and one strap of her nightgown, revealing the creamy curve of her shoulder and one rounded rosy-tipped breast.

'*Bellissima*,' he whispered. His mouth was gentle on her body, so gentle that fear began to recede and give way to a warm, insidious pleasure, so gentle that she could almost forget that she was not the first woman whose body had come alive under his practised touch. Almost, but not quite. Summoning a desperate strength from some inner recess of her being, she thrust him away from her and slid to the floor on to her knees. Instinct told her she ought to run away from him—into the bathroom where she could lock herself in, perhaps, but her trembling legs wouldn't support her that far and she knew it. All she was capable of was kneeling there almost at his feet, murmuring 'No, Santino, please, no,' like an incantation while the tears she had suppressed earlier slid unchecked down her white face.

He said something half under his breath that sounded as if he was swearing. She saw his hand reach down to her and shrank back, and at the same moment there came a persistent knocking at the outer door of the suite.

There was a pause, then Santino swung himself off the bed and walked across the room to the door. Juliet heard him cross the sitting room and answer the door, and then the murmur of voices and the chink of a trolley as it was wheeled in. She heard the waiter leave, and the sound of Santino's footsteps returning. She was still incapable of running or hiding. She leaned her head against the side of the bed and waited, wearily, to see what he would do.

He halted in the doorway. His face looked remote, like that of a stranger.

'I suppose I must apologise,' he said after a pause that seemed endless. 'My only excuse, Giulietta, is that you made me very angry. But there's no need to be frightened. It won't happen again. Now come and eat or your soup will be cold.'

He came across to her and lifted her to her feet, his arm impersonal. She let him lead her out of the room and across to where the trolley stood waiting in front of the sofa. He seated her, unfolded a linen table napkin and handed it to her, then ladled some of the rich fragrant mixture from the tureen into the delicate china bowl that stood waiting.

'I'll leave you now,' he said when he had completed these preparations. 'Shall I ask my mother to look in on you when she retires for the night?'

Juliet shook her head wordlessly. She did not trust her voice.

'Very well,' he said. '*Buona sera, Giulietta.*'

He waited for a moment and when she did not reply, walked without hurry across to the door and out without looking back.

Juliet sat motionless staring at the steaming bowl of soup in front of her. Long after it had gone cold, she got to her feet and went back into the bedroom. She let the peignoir drop in a crumpled heap to the floor and climbed in between the covers of the tumbled bed. She felt very cold suddenly, and very tired, although she knew she was beyond sleep.

And as she lay there, counting each hour chimed out by a nearby campanile, through the open door from the sitting room came drifting the tormenting, evocative perfume of Santino's roses.

CHAPTER EIGHT

'DARLING,' wrote Mim, 'I'm so pleased that you've managed to extend your holiday for so long. You'll be able to see such a lot of Italy. Now aren't you glad that I persuaded you to go? And how nice that Jan has been able to get some time off with you. How kind of these friends of hers to have invited you both to stay with them.

'Jan's news is really exciting,' the letter continued. 'She's been very happy at Di Lorenzo, but I can quite see that the time has come for her to make a change, and how wonderful to think that there's talk of a film!'

Juliet put the rest of the letter back in the envelope and stared rather bleakly out of her bedroom window. So that was Jan's latest line, she thought bitterly. If only it were true, or even approaching the truth. The fact was that Jan was now out of work. She had officially resigned from Di Lorenzo, and had written to several other fashion houses stating she was available for work, and giving a forward date some two months after the expected birth of her baby. But none of them had shown even a modicum of interest in availing themselves of her services, and Jan's mood had grown progressively stormier at each politely worded refusal.

She had seemed more contented of late, Juliet had to admit, but there had been no approaches made to her about future work, and certainly none from a film company. She sighed. Jan enjoyed the limelight, and was not going to be prepared to live her life quietly in anyone else's background.

They had been at the *castello* for just over a month, and the time was fast approaching when Juliet knew she was going to have to return to England. It had been far from the happiest period of her life. In fact she could not remember when she had been more actively miserable. Yet on the surface, everything in the garden appeared lovely. What had gone wrong?

Acting the role of Santino's fiancée had not been as difficult as she feared, because he had gone out of his way, it seemed, to make it easy for her. He had been away on business a great deal, and apart from kissing her lightly on arrival and departure, he had kept his word about not forcing his attentions upon her. There had been, she thought with a certain relief, no return to that dark, frightening passion he had shown her that night in the hotel suite. In fact, there had been no passion at all, and Santino seemed to make a point of avoiding being alone with her. She supposed, rather desolately, that she should be grateful for this. It was after all what she had wanted—or rather what she had told him she wanted, so she had no one to thank but herself if he had taken her at her word.

Not that they had had much opportunity to be alone since their return to the *castello* because Jan was always there—glamorous, confident, and often with a faint mocking smile curving her lips as she observed them. Sometimes,

Juliet thought her sister knew that the engagement was merely a hoax. Sometimes when they were sitting round the dining table and Jan would make one of her lightly barbed remarks about love and marriage, Juliet felt like crying aloud, 'Oh, please let's stop all this pretence. We don't need it now.'

Not, she supposed, that that was strictly true. During their sojourn at the *castello*, they had received two seemingly casual visits from Vittoria Leontana. She was all smiles and affection for Jan, and even managed a few cordial phrases in English for Juliet, but it was clear she had come to snoop, and Juliet was thankful for the adroit way in which Jan managed to evade her more searching questions. It was plain that the Contessa had seen the newspaper story Santino had planted linking his name with Jan's, and that she was not prepared to accept that it was merely a journalistic error, confusing one sister for another. But in the end, she had to depart with her obvious curiosity about the situation still unsatisfied, and Juliet found herself breathing a sigh of relief as her expensive car turned out of the courtyard and drove away along the coast.

She had sometimes wondered if the Contessa had been responsible for the phalanx of photographers waiting at the clinic steps for them to leave that day four weeks earlier. She had been startled by the battery of flash-bulbs and turned away with a slight gasp, but Jan had revelled in the situation, managing a brave smile for the cameras, and clinging to Santino's arm as if he was her one rock and salvation.

Juliet had expected Santino to be angry at the reception committee, but although he had not loitered, he had answered the questions they fired at him quite patiently.

During the drive back to Roccaforte, at a time when she was sure Jan who had been given painkillers for the trip was safely asleep, Juliet had ventured to ask Santino what the reporters' questions had been about.

He gave a slight shrug. 'About *la bella* Janina, for the most part,' he answered shortly. 'How badly was she injured? When will she return to her modelling career? You can imagine the sort of thing.' He gave her a sideways glance. 'And they asked about you, of course.'

'I see.' She looked down at her hands, clasped together in her lap. 'Did—did you tell them that we were—engaged?'

'Naturally,' he said with a touch of impatience. 'I told them exactly the same story that we have told everyone else. What did you expect?'

She sighed. 'Exactly that, I suppose,' she admitted in a low voice. 'I—I just wish that not quite so many people had to know. It's going to make things so awkward when——' she paused, not knowing how to finish the sentence.

'When we decide this particular comedy is over, you mean,' he said in a hard voice. 'Don't worry about it, *cara*. I will make it clear to all sources that it was you that jilted me, if that's what you're afraid of.'

'It isn't,' she whispered. 'For one thing, I'm worried in case the English newspapers do get hold of it, and Mim sees it.'

'Hmm.' He was silent for a moment. 'Perhaps it would be better if you wrote to her yourself and told her that we were engaged?'

'No!' Juliet was vehement. 'I'd have to tell her everything in that case. I can't tell her that I'm engaged to be married—she'd be so thrilled, so excited. It wouldn't be fair to hoax her. Besides, she'd want to meet you. There would be all sorts of complications.'

'Then we must hope that the English newspapers decide that your affairs are of no interest to them,' he said rather drily, and she subsided back into her seat, flushing a little.

Now that they were in league, however temporarily, there seemed to be a barrier between them that had never existed when she was fighting with him. His manner was cool and courteous, and this in itself was sufficient to keep her at bay. She tried to tell herself that it was better—easier this way, but she could not make herself believe it. Nothing he could say or do—no hardening of his attitude to her could make the ending of this thing either simple or bearable. She was caught in an emotional snare which was tearing at her.

At nights she lay awake, staring into the darkness, telling herself that it was madness to allow herself to feel this way for a man whom, in all conscience, she hardly knew. He's a stranger, she cried out silently, a stranger, and yet at the same time she knew that this was hardly the truth. That it was as if she had always known him, always in some strange way been waiting for him. Her tragedy was that he did not feel the same. At first she had been an aggravation, something on his list requiring immediate attention, then later an available woman to be made love to as and when the mood took him. At times she even found herself wishing bitterly that she belonged to his world, and could accept the kind of casual encounter that clearly was as much as he wanted in a relationship. But it was useless. She wanted more, and she had to face the fact that she had nothing to hope for from him.

She stared out of her window along to the beach. There was a gaily coloured beach umbrella erected there now, and she could see Jan's distant figure taking her ease in its shade. She had little doubt that if she looked hard enough she would be able to pick out Santino as well, but she had no real wish to add reinforcement to an already increasing awareness of the attraction that existed between her sister and the man she loved.

At first she had told herself it was completely one-sided,

and had cringed inwardly from the blatancy of Jan's pursuit of Santino. Nothing—and especially not the fact that as far as she knew he belonged to her sister—appeared to deter her, not even the cool amusement with which her first overtures had been received. And eventually her persistence had paid off. Jan had always been lovely, but now her early pregnancy had lent her face a new softness and her skin a bloom and radiance that had been lacking before. Apart from an extra fullness to her breasts, her body had not begun to alter yet, and as she sunbathed every day, her skin had turned to a soft shade of honey tan which was most becoming to her. Just how becoming, a man like Santino could not fail to appreciate, Juliet thought bitterly.

At first she had joined the sunbathing parties on the beach, but gradually she had begun to feel more and more *de trop*. She had not thought it was deliberate at first. After all, Jan would obviously know a great many people whom Santino would also number among his acquaintance. She had moved in a smart, fashionable world that he also knew, so it was natural that they would have things in common to talk about. But Juliet had not expected to feel so completely excluded. She had not been disturbed at first by Jan's frequent lapses into Italian, usually airily explained away by her sister as—'A joke, sweetie. It just wouldn't sound funny in English.' She could even accept that. What she could not accept was the gradual switch in their relationships which put Jan at his side at mealtimes, her voice low and intimate as she retailed some amusing or scandalous anecdote which might as well have been in ancient Chinese for all the meaning it had for Juliet. It was skilfully done, of course, with frequent contrite looks at Juliet. 'Darling, you mustn't let me monopolise your gorgeous fiancé.'

Nevertheless, Juliet thought, that was precisely and quite cold-bloodedly what Jan was doing, and the fact that the engagement did not actually exist between Santino and her-

self did not really make her sister's actions any less repre-
hensible. As far as Jan knew, Juliet and Santino had fallen
in love, and she was doing her level best to intervene. At
times, Juliet wondered rather despairingly what her motives
could be. She couldn't possibly hope that Santino would
marry her, however strong the physical attraction might be
between them.

But Juliet had not bargained for Santino's reaction to her
sister's transparently provocative advances. She had expected him to brush them aside contemptuously, but he
gave no sign of doing so. He might still be faintly amused,
but he was never discouraging, and Juliet suspected miserably that but for her presence they might well be in the
throes of an affair by now.

With every day that passed, she knew more overwhelm-
ingly than ever that all she could do to avoid more heartbreak was to get out and go back to England. But this still
presented problems. Santino gave no sign that he was prepared to let her go just yet. At times, she wondered if the
humiliation she had suffered over the past few weeks was
intended to punish her for the deception she had practised
on him. She was no longer sure of anything, except the
lonely ache deep inside her.

There were also practical problems standing in the way
of her immediate departure. She was still having to make
do with the assortment of clothes that Santino had collected
from the apartment that first night. Her handbag with her
passport and money, and the rest of her clothes were still
at the apartment. And while Jan was plentifully supplied
with clothes—Juliet guessed that the set of matched luggage
reposing in her room contained the trousseau she had
bought for Mario—that did not prevent her from making
slightly edged remarks when Juliet appeared in anything
from her wardrobe. And unfortunately the majority of garments that Santino had selected belonged to Jan. She had

tried to raise this point with Santino a few times, but he had impatiently brushed it aside.

Roccaforte was a tiny fishing village, he said coldly, not a fashionable resort.

Juliet looked down at her mother's envelope still clutched in her hand and her eyes blurred with sudden tears at the sight of the dear, familiar writing. That was where she belonged, she told herself bleakly, back among the small dramas of the staff room and high street. She could cope with those. Here, she was out of her emotional depth, but at least she had the sense to know it.

There was nothing else for it. She would have to tackle Santino about fixing a date for her return to England. After all, the autumn term would be starting very soon, and she would have to be back in her classroom for that.

Nor was there any point in putting the interview off to a more opportune moment. She never really knew from one day to the next whether Santino was going to be there or not, and when he was there, Jan was never far away either so she had little hope of any real privacy to say what she had to.

She felt self-conscious and miserable as she left the road and walked across the yielding sand towards them. She knew they had seen her and were watching her approach, and she had an uncomfortable instinct that she had intruded. As she neared them she saw that Santino, who was lying only about a foot away from Jan, had propped himself up on his elbow, and that his mouth was twisted impatiently. Jan was talking in that low, laughing voice she seemed to reserve for him, but as Juliet came up to them, she broke off rather theatrically and smiled up at her.

'Hello, sweetie. Are you joining us? How nice. I thought you'd be writing back to Mim like a dutiful daughter.'

Juliet made herself smile back. 'There seems little point,'

she said coolly. 'I can probably get there myself ahead of a letter.'

She did not look at Santino as she spoke but kept her eyes fixed on Jan, noticing that her sister's gaze flickered a little at her words. She hoped that Santino would say something, but he remained silent, and she supposed that he was either wilfully ignoring what she had just said, or merely indifferent. She sighed inwardly. His attitude was not making her task any easier. She made herself turn to him. He had removed his shirt, and the close-fitting denim pants he wore clung to his muscular legs. Dark glasses hid the expression in his eyes as he looked up at her, but she knew intuitively that he was annoyed at the interruption.

She felt a little spurt of anger rise within her. How dared he behave like this? He had forced her to agree to this fake engagement, and had been quick to demand certain standards of behaviour from her, she thought bitterly. She made herself smile down at him.

'Could I have a word with you—darling?' She had to force the word past suddenly dry lips. 'I hardly seem to see you nowadays.'

For a moment, he seemed to hesitate, then he rose to his feet. 'You will excuse us, Janina?'

'Of course,' Jan leaned back on her cushions, smiling. 'I mustn't be selfish about my enjoyment of your company. I mustn't forget that you belong to Julie.'

Santino glanced at Juliet and his teeth showed momentarily in a smile that was more like a sneer. 'So I do,' he said lightly. 'Will a stroll along the beach content you, *mia*, or would you prefer to return to the *castello*?'

'The beach will be fine,' she said, trying not to let her hurt show in her voice. 'I—I won't keep you.'

She walked stiffly beside him, knowing that Jan was watching them go.

'So you've sought me out at last,' he said coldly when they were at last out of earshot. 'I suppose I should be flattered. May I know the reason for this sudden desire for my company?'

'You can hardly complain that you've lacked female companionship,' she returned stormily, goaded by his tone.

'No, I can't—and I don't, believe me.' His voice was satirical. 'Are you here in the role of outraged *fidanzata* to complain that I am spending too much time with your sister?'

Juliet bent her head so that her hair swung like a curtain across her face, concealing her expression from him. She was afraid that something of the pang of real pain his words had caused her might show on her face.

'I don't think we need take this—charade quite to those extremes,' she said, trying to match his own tone. 'You are a free agent, and I—well, I can no longer see that I'm doing the slightest good by remaining here.'

'I believe that our arrangement was that you should continue to be engaged to me until Mario and Francesca were married,' he said sharply.

'Was that it?' she shrugged. 'I really don't remember. But if you insist on going on with this, I'm afraid that you'll have to be contented with an engagement at a distance. I have to return to work. I'm a schoolteacher, if you remember, and the school year starts in England in a matter of days.'

'But the wedding—Mario's wedding. You will return for that?'

'Hardly.' She shook her head.

'But my mother will be expecting you to be there.'

'I fail to see why,' she said wearily. 'I think, on the contrary, that she'll probably give three rousing cheers when she hears I've returned home. Besides, it will be—much easier for you to tell everyone the engagement is over once I'm back in England. You can tell them I decided I couldn't settle in Italy, perhaps.'

'Thank you,' he said, his voice like ice. 'I think I can

manage to prepare a story that will satisfy the curious.' His
hand shot out and gripped hers so tightly that she had to
suppress a little cry of pain. 'Don't pull away, *cara*,' he
grated. 'The performance is not yet at an end, and we are
happy lovers strolling along a sunlit beach hand in hand.'
She shivered at the molten anger in his voice. 'Tell me, is
your anxiety for your pupils the only reason for this sudden
urge to return to England?'

'Not entirely,' she said slowly, afraid of saying too much,
but also of revealing too much by her silence. 'There are
other reasons.'

'And am I aware of those reasons?' He stopped suddenly
and swung her round so that she was standing in front of
him with his arms linked round her waist. To a casual ob-
server, their stance would look like a lighthearted embrace.
Only Juliet knew that the arms that held her felt like a vice
against her flesh, and that there was no softness on the dark
face that stared down into hers. She felt he was looking
through her into her very soul, and that there was not a
thought or an emotion that was hidden from him, and the
thought shamed her to the core of her being.

'You may be,' she said wretchedly. What did he want her
to say? she asked herself bitterly. To admit her love and
grovel at his feet, begging him to be merciful?

'So your sister was right,' he said softly, and she felt a
deep mortified blush suffuse her face. Had Jan guessed her
secret, she thought confusedly, and passed it on during one
of those laughing intimate conversations of theirs?

'Poor little Julie.' She could hear the words in her head.
'She's so dreadfully in love with you. She'll make a wonder-
fully submissive wife.' And then Santino, his perceptions
sharpened by the hint, watching her, noting the give-away
signs she probably wasn't even aware of. She wanted to say,
yes, but it doesn't matter. I won't cling or be an embarrassment, just let me go—but the words wouldn't come. The

soft sounds of the day, the wash of the sea at her feet, the
distant laughter of children, were all suddenly magnified
and intensified, and over them all, Santino was saying
bleakly, 'Did you imagine she wouldn't tell me?'

'I didn't even realise that she knew,' she said, and paused,
appalled at the extent of the confession she had just made.
She made a little awkward movement of her hands. 'I'm
sorry. But it surely doesn't matter. If you'll just let me
go ...'

His arms fell away from her, and she thought for a
moment that he had mistaken her meaning, but then he
spoke.

'I've let you go already,' he said harshly. 'Haven't you
noticed?'

She looked up at him, realising for the first time that this
was why he had been avoiding her, devoting his free time at
the *castello* to Jan instead. Being cruel to be kind, she told
herself dazedly. Letting her see at once that she had nothing
to hope for. Probably wondering to himself why her pride
hadn't driven her away days ago.

It came to her rescue now, stiffening her spine and lifting
her chin, and she was thankful for it.

'Then let's not waste any more time,' she said coolly.
'There's only one snag—my passport and money are still at
Jan's apartment, with the rest of my clothes. I would like to
pick them up.'

He gestured impatiently. 'There is no need. I will collect
them. I have to go to Rome tomorrow, and I will return
them to you here.' He stared at her again and she was glad
that she could not see the look in his eyes behind those enigmatic glasses because it might have been pity. 'If—if you
are sure that is what you want.'

'Quite sure,' she said, and managed a smile.

She heard him take a quick breath as if he was going to
say something, then stop. For a moment he stood motion-

less, an odd tension about his body, then he gave a faint shrug. 'Then there is nothing more to be said.'

He turned and walked away from her back to where Jan was lying. Juliet could see that she had turned on to her front and unfastened the top half of her bikini. As Santino dropped down beside her he ran a finger down the curve of her spine, and Juliet heard her little laughing protest in response.

Jealousy, that harsh destructive emotion, tore at her being, and she thought, 'Oh, please let me go from here soon. I can't stand it any longer.'

But it appeared that she had to stand that and more, for when she went downstairs to breakfast the following morning it was to find herself alone except for a disgruntled Annunziata. Disbelievingly, she was given to understand that the Signore had already left for Rome, and that her sister had gone with him.

Juliet drank her coffee, feeling as if she had been publicly slapped in the face. And the situation was not helped by Annunziata's unspoken but nevertheless overt sympathy.

She spent a forlorn day wandering along the shore, toying with the appetising food Annunziata anxiously set in front of her, and finally, in a determined effort to do something positive about her departure, sorting her clothes from Jan's and hanging those that did not belong to her in the guest room her sister was occupying. But for how long? she wondered. Probably as soon as she had left, Jan would move into Santino's room.

She had no idea how long the journey to Rome and back would take, but it was nevertheless a shock when evening came and she found herself eating a solitary dinner. When the meal was over, she tried to listen to some music on the stereo, but nothing in Santino's enormous record collection seemed to have any appeal, and when her choice was finally made, she found her ear was keyed over the top of the music for the sound of a car approaching along the coast road.

She could hardly believe it when she glanced at her watch and found that it was past midnight, and for the first time it occurred to her that they might not return that night. She flinched inwardly as the thought and all its implications manifested itself. She wandered round the room, going to the window every few minutes and staring out into the velvety blackness, hoping to see it slashed by powerful headlights. She tried to remember other trips Santino had taken, and how long he had been away, but her mind refused to work properly. She sat down in a corner of the sofa and tried to make herself relax, but all the time she was on edge, listening for the sound of the car.

She had no idea at what hour her weariness and unhappiness translated itself into sleep, but the next thing she knew it was daylight and Annunziata, her face furrowed with worry, was bending over her, shaking her shoulder insistently.

'*Ecco l'auto, signorina,*' she announced.

Juliet sat up, wincing from cramped muscles. Her first thought was flight. It would be dreadful for Santino and Jan to walk in and find her sitting there waiting for them. Besides, she felt untidy and dishevelled after her uncomfortable night, and did not want anyone to see her looking like this. She was halfway up the stairs with Annunziata busily undoing the bolts on the great door when something prompted her to turn and look down on the scene below. The same kind of motive that prompts one to bite on an aching tooth, she told herself bitterly.

But it was not Santino's tall figure who entered as the door swung open. It was the Signora. Nor was she alone. Her husband was just behind her, and a young dark-haired girl whom Juliet had never seen before. She turned to make her escape but it was too late.

'So you are there, *mia figlia*. Come here to me,' the Signora ordered, and Juliet very reluctantly obeyed.

She was subjected to a critical glance from head to foot. 'What is this?' the Signora demanded. 'Your eyes are red, and you are *molto pallida*. Also your clothes are creased. What meaning is this?'

Well aware that Annunziata was standing nearby bursting to give any information that she failed to provide, Juliet said, 'I—I fell asleep on the sofa last night.'

'Are there no beds in this place?' the Signora enquired. 'And where is my son who permits such a thing?'

Before Juliet could answer, Annunziata stepped forward and took the initiative. As she proceeded, Juliet saw a dark frown appear on the Signora's brow, and eventually she silenced Annunziata with a slight gesture.

'So he is in Rome,' she said, turning to Juliet. 'Why not you also?'

Juliet moved her shoulders wearily. She found this interrogation embarrassing, particularly in front of this young stranger, although judging by the puzzled expression on her charming oval face, she did not understand much of it.

'Because he didn't ask me to,' she answered bluntly, then forcing a smile turned to Signor Peretto and asked whether they had had breakfast.

The Signora belatedly recalled her social obligations. 'Francesca, come here,' she ordered. 'I wish to present you to Giulietta who is to marry Santino.'

'No.' Juliet shook her head. Under the circumstances she couldn't go on with this charade any longer, she decided. 'We—we have decided that we should only make each other miserable, *signora*, and I—have decided to return to England.'

'This I do not understand,' the Signora said roundly. 'Later you shall explain. But now go and take off that crumpled dress.'

Juliet was more than happy to obey. As she went back up the stairs, she could feel the puzzled gaze of the girl Francesca boring into her back, and could understand her bewilderment. Presumably she had been brought here to meet her future sister-in-law, only to learn that it had been a wasted journey. In a way, Juliet felt almost regretful. Francesca had a sweet face and gentle eyes, and on a different occasion, under other circumstances, she would have enjoyed making her acquaintance.

She had a quick bath, and changed into a flared cream skirt and a long-sleeved navy silk shirt before making her way downstairs again. Annunziata was serving coffee and hot rolls, and the Signora gestured to Juliet to join them. Juliet was half afraid that another inquisition was about to start, but instead the Signora chatted amiably about the forthcoming wedding, about guest lists and china, and the bishop who had agreed to perform the ceremony. Stealing a glance at Francesca under her lashes while this recital was going on, Juliet thought she had never seen a girl look quite so glowingly radiant at the prospect of her wedding, and she was thankful in her heart that all her scheming had come to nothing, and that she had not managed to prevent Mario from marrying a girl who was clearly besotted about him. She hoped very much that Francesca would never hear about his lapse, and was glad that Jan was miles away in Rome at this moment.

When breakfast was over the Signora ordered her husband to take Francesca round the *castello*, and Juliet knew that the interrogation could not be deferred any longer.

'Show her everything,' was the Signora's last instruction as the pair prepared to depart. 'I have things to say to Giulietta.' She watched them leave the room, then turned to the clearly apprehensive girl in front of her.

'Now you explain,' she ordered. 'Until now, I think you

marry my Santino. Now you say you not marry. Why? Do
you no longer love him?'

Juliet felt a gasp rise in her throat and suppressed it
hastily. So her well-kept secret had in fact been an open
book to everyone, she thought unhappily, and there was no
point in making any denials under the Signora's shrewd
gaze. They would not be believed.

'It isn't that.' She bent her head. 'But you see Santino
doesn't really want to marry me.'

'You speak of that tale he tells me—that he proposed only
because he has dishonoured you.' The Signora made a small
contemptuous noise. 'I do not believe that. Santino is a man
of today. As I tell myself later, he does not care for such
things. Besides,' she added, 'you are the sister of that other
one. What does my family owe you? Nothing!'

She saw Juliet flush miserably and patted her hand. 'I
should not have said that. My son tells me you are different
and I believe him. So why will you not marry him?'

'You don't understand.' Juliet realised that complete
frankness was the only answer. 'We never were—really
engaged. It was just a story we made up.' Wearily she
explained why Santino had insisted on the pseudo-
engagement.

The Signora heard her out, open-mouthed. 'Then why
did he not tell me this?' she demanded.

'I don't know.' Juliet shook her head. 'He—he said that
I was to tell no one that it—it was a hoax. And I haven't
—until now. Only I'm going away— tomorrow, I hope, and
it probably doesn't matter any more.'

The Signora sat frowning darkly. 'And my Santino is in
Rome with that other one, your sister?' She cast the
heavens a malevolent glance. 'And to think that I blessed
myself that I had one son not a fool!'

'Don't blame Santino,' Juliet said with some difficulty.
'He—he didn't intend that it should work out like this.'

'Who knows what he intended?' the Signora said acidly. 'I doubt if he know himself.' She studied Juliet for a moment and her expression softened. 'So you love my son,' she said gently. 'Well, is simple. Stay here and marry him. Tell that other one, your sister, to go run a jump.'

Juliet felt more like crying, but she found herself smiling unwillingly.

'I—I can't do that, signora. And Santino doesn't want me. He would have—taken me when he thought I was Jan, but it all changed when he discovered the truth. I—I really must get away. It will be easier all round if I do.'

'But will it be easy for you?' The Signora gave Juliet a long questioning look, and shook her head at what she saw. 'Do not do this thing, piccina,' she urged gently. 'Stay and fight.'

Juliet sighed. 'I have nothing to fight for, signora,' she said simply. 'It's better if I just—go, believe me.'

All day they waited for Santino to return, and at last, as evening approached, the Signora yielded to her husband's persuasions and agreed to return to the villa outside Messina where they were staying with Francesca's aunt and her family. She would, she said, return, however, and the promise was uttered in a tone that boded ill for Santino.

Juliet had finished dinner and was sitting alone in the salotto telling herself that another night on the sofa was out of the question, when she heard the sound of the car. For a moment she felt like flight, then she clenched her hands into fists and sat down again, hiding them in the folds of her skirts.

Jan came in first. She was laughing as she entered, and it seemed to Juliet's over-stretched nerves that there was a note of triumph in that laugh. She checked when she saw her sister's quiet figure.

'Darling,' she said, 'how sweet! Sitting around like faithful Penelope!' She sauntered across to the sofa and sat down at the other end of it, raising her arms languorously above her head.

'It has been,' she murmured, a tantalising smile playing about the corners of her mouth 'Quite some trip.'

Juliet forced her stiff mouth to work. 'I didn't know you were going.'

Jan's smile widened. She had all the appearance of the cat who has had the cream and intends to make the saucer hers as well. 'Santino was most insistent, sweetie,' she said gaily. 'To be frank—and I know you won't mind my mentioning it—I think he finds this engagement of yours a teeny bit of a bore. I expect it seemed like a good idea at the time. Well, he may get engaged on the spur of the moment, but he certainly won't get married in the same way.' She paused, but Juliet said nothing, so after a minute she continued gently, 'Just one more thing, darling. I really wouldn't wear my heart on my sleeve quite so openly. That little scene on the beach—dragging him off with you like that when you could see he didn't want to go—not awfully dignified, my love. Learn to be a good loser.'

Juliet rose to her feet. 'I don't think I want to learn anything, thank you,' she said quite courteously. 'I shall be leaving here in the morning anyway. But before I go, there's one thing I must say, Jan, although I never thought I would for Mim's sake. You are without doubt the biggest bitch I've ever met, and I very much hope that I never have to set eyes on you again, sister or not.' It was her turn to smile then at the look of utter astonishment on Jan's lovely face. 'And please ask Santino not to disturb me tonight,' she went on. 'If he would just leave my money and passport here in the *salotto*, I'll collect it on my way out.'

'Don't be a fool,' Jan said icily. 'How do you propose getting out of this dead-and-alive hole unless he takes you?'

'I'll find a way,' Juliet said. 'I'd rather walk back to Rome in my bare feet in any case than ask either of you for the slightest favour.'

She heard a slight movement behind her and turned to see Santino standing in the doorway. Judging by the grim look on his face, there was little doubt he had clearly heard her last remark.

Juliet turned and made for the stairs, not faltering when his voice rang after her. 'Giulietta!'

She took no notice. She was just setting foot on the bottom stair when he caught her.

Furiously she shook his detaining hand from her arm. 'Please let go of me!'

'I have some things to say to you.' He needed a shave, she noticed, and his face betrayed a lack of sleep. She bit her lip as her reason told her the obvious explanation.

'I don't want to hear them,' she said in a low voice. 'I have some good advice to pass on to you, Santino. Learn to be a good loser.' She went on up the stairs, leaving him standing there, and there was nothing in the world that would have made her look back.

'Juliet darling.' Her mother shook her shoulder gently. 'It's past eight o'clock. Didn't you hear your alarm? I've brought you a cup of tea.'

'Oh, heavens!' Juliet sat up wearily, pushing her hair back. 'Thanks, Mim, you're an angel, but I've hardly got time to drink it.'

'Oh, yes, you have,' Mrs Laurence said firmly. 'You may have dropped the habit of having breakfast these days—which I don't approve of, by the way—but you're not leaving this house without at least a hot drink inside you, my girl, and that's final.'

Juliet smiled up into her mother's lovingly exasperated countenance.

'To hear is to obey, O Queen,' she murmured wickedly.

'That's more like it.' Mrs Laurence sat down on the edge of the bed and contemplated her daughter, her eyes filled with an anxiety she no longer took any pains to conceal. 'I've been wondering over the past few weeks whether I'd ever see you smile again.'

'Oh, Mim!' Juliet sipped at the hot tea. 'Surely, it hasn't been that bad?'

Mrs Laurence smiled slightly. 'It has from where I've been standing,' she said gently. 'Darling, would it help if we talked about it—whatever it is? I gather it must be something that happened while you were abroad, considering that's been a taboo subject since you returned.'

Juliet set down her cup and saucer on the bedside table. 'There's really nothing to discuss,' she said too brightly. 'And I must be getting up. I'm late as it is and . . .'

Her mother pushed her gently back against the pillows. 'Then an extra five minutes won't make much difference either way,' she decreed. 'All I know is that after living with a stranger all this time, I caught a glimpse of the old Juliet, and I want her back—for good.'

Juliet sighed. 'I don't think she exists any more, Mim,' she said rather drearily.

'Then what happened to her?' Mrs Laurence pressed. 'My daughter comes home from what should have been the holiday of a lifetime like a ghost of her former self. I haven't heard you laugh since you've been back. I've barely seen you smile. I can't imagine what poor Barry must be thinking.'

Juliet bent her head. 'I'm afraid that doesn't particularly concern me,' she said quietly.

'I see.' Her mother gave her a sharp glance. 'So it's a man. Are you going to tell me who he is?'

Juliet shook her head. 'There—there's no point. I shan't be seeing him again.'

'Don't you want to?'

'It isn't a question of what I want,' Juliet said tiredly. 'We want different things, that's all.' She tried to smile. 'And I soon found I wasn't on his list.'

'Oh, darling!' Mrs Laurence laid her hand over Juliet's. There were tears in her eyes. 'Why in the world did I ever persuade you to go?'

Juliet squeezed her mother's fingers. 'I'm glad you did. It—it's been a salutory experience if nothing else.' She smiled waveringly. 'Actually, I made rather a fool of myself. I let myself fall for him without really knowing him. You can't be in love with someone—the kind of love that matters anyway—in the space of a few hours, can you?'

'I knew I was in love with your father twenty-four hours after I met him,' Mrs Laurence said surprisingly. 'It took him a little longer,' she added, a smile of tender reminiscence lighting her eyes.

Juliet swallowed. 'But there was nothing to prevent your marrying Daddy, was there? There were no—obstacles?'

'No.' Her mother frowned, trying to remember. 'The usual tiffs and misunderstandings, of course, but ...' She stopped and her eyes came to rest on Juliet with a worried expression. 'Oh, darling. He—he isn't married?'

'No,' Juliet hastened to reassure her. 'Nor likely to be. He—he isn't the marrying kind,' she added after a brief pause.

'I never knew a man that was,' Mrs Laurence said rather drily. 'Are you so sure that there's no hope? I can't believe that the kind of fly-by-night relationship you've portrayed would be enough to wipe the light out of your eyes. You've lost weight. You've shadows under your eyes. If it wasn't for your tan, you'd be looking ill. It will be half-term in a few weeks,' she went on hesitatingly. 'Why don't you go back—see him? Settle this thing, or get him out of your system once and for all.'

'No!' Juliet was aghast. 'No—I can never go back. I

wish I could explain, Mim,' she added wretchedly, a sob
rising in her throat. 'But I can't, so please don't say any
more.'

'It's Jan, isn't it?' Mrs Laurence asked, a touch of grim-
ness in her voice. 'You've barely mentioned her either since
you've been home. Is it her fault that it's gone wrong for
you?'

Caught off guard by her mother's perceptiveness, Juliet
parried, 'I—I don't know what you mean.'

'So I'm right.' Mrs Laurence shook her head. 'Oh, my
dear, I'm sorry.'

Juliet gave a humourless laugh. 'There's nothing to be
sorry about. It's hardly odd that he should prefer her.' She
bit her lip as an image of Jan, triumphantly beautiful after
her night in Rome with Santino, in the *salotto* of the
castello, rose up in front of her. 'She is—very lovely.'

'And very selfish—and very greedy.' Mrs Laurence
stifled a sigh as Juliet gave her a quick amazed stare. 'You
surely didn't imagine I thought she was perfect? I know her
faults, as well as I know my own, but I thought she would
have spared you—her own sister.'

Juliet moved restlessly. 'Let's not talk about it any more,'
she appealed with difficulty. 'I must get up now, Mim. I
have to get ready for school.'

As she washed and dressed, Juliet found her thoughts unwillingly returning to that last night she had spent under
Santino's roof. Sometimes she wondered what would have
happened if she had turned and looked at him, and she
fantasised that he might have held his arms out to her. And
what would she have done? Well, she knew the answer to
that. She would have gone to him unthinkingly, uncaringly,
in spite of everything that lay between them.

As it was, she had gone to her room and bolted the door,
and she did not open it all that long wakeful night, although
someone who might have been Annunziata came and

knocked very gently about an hour later.

She had spent much of the night worrying about how she was going to get back to Rome. Bravado was one thing, but reality and common sense quite another. But in the morning, like a small elegant good fairy, the Signora had arrived, and almost before she knew what was happening Juliet found herself ensconced in the back of Signor Peretto's luxurious car, with the *castello* a dwindling speck in the distance behind her.

Of Santino there had been no sign, and she had no means of knowing what the Signora had said to him, or whether she had said anything at all. She was thankful to have her bag with her money and passport and return air ticket, and told herself all she had to worry about now was finding a seat on a flight home. But even here all her problems were smoothed away. She guessed afterwards that Signor Peretto had pulled some strings, because a seat on the first flight out miraculously became available. He and the Signora had been very kind, she thought, but at the same time it was more than evident that they wanted to be rid of her. Nor could she particularly blame them for that in the light of all that had happened.

Her reunion with Mim had been an ordeal in many ways. There was so much that had to be left unsaid, but until this morning she had thought she had made a skilful enough job of the half-truths and evasions she had been forced to employ.

Work, she'd told herself, was what she needed, and with only a few days to collect together the material she needed for the start of term, she wouldn't have time to think. But it hadn't worked out that way. Even when she was absorbed in what she was doing, and later, when she had got the children busy and interested, she would find her thoughts suddenly straying back to the *castello*, and its dark imperious owner, and the agony would begin again as her imagination ran riot, painting pictures of Jan and Santino intimately alone at the *castello*.

And it was an agony, such as she had never known, although she had caught a glimpse of it that night when she had sat alone and known that they were staying in Rome together. But that was nothing to what she had suffered since. Had she really thought that distance and separation would help to drive him out of her mind and heart? She must have been mad even to entertain such a wild hope. All it meant was that she relived over and over again in her memory every moment she had spent with him, every word he had said. But it was the moments when his lovemaking returned to torment her that were the hardest of all to bear, especially when she knew there would never be a consummation of that lovemaking—that she would never belong to him as she had wanted to belong.

And it was little consolation to tell herself that even if she had given herself to him, nothing would have changed. She would still be back here in England with her memories —and perhaps some regrets as well.

She arrived at school, breathless, just as the bell for assembly was ringing, and her lateness made her on edge for the rest of the day. She had a curious sensation that she was waiting for something to happen, but her sense of anticipation was not a pleasant one. She didn't have her usual patience with the children either. Several times she snapped back in answer to a question, and she could see them eyeing her covertly, their small surprised faces reflecting how unused they were to finding her in this sort of mood. Her conscience led her to cancel the project work she had planned for the afternoon, and let them have a long messy art session instead, followed by an instalment of the serial story that she was reading to them. It was a disorganised afternoon, but it seemed to be what they all needed, for Juliet felt al-

most at peace as she walked out of the school gates that
evening and turned for home.

It had been a fine day, and the air was still quite warm,
so she decided she would have a quick tea and then spend a
couple of hours in the garden. Mim's roses were still a
picture, but it was time to make plans for the coming spring
—safe plans that had everything to do with regeneration
and growth, and nothing at all to say about emotions.

She was so deep in thought as she walked up the road
that she scarcely noticed the car parked in the road outside
her house at first. And when she did see it, it was with a
growing puzzlement rather than any instant recognition,
as if her imagination was playing her tricks. Because it was
Santino's car.

She stood at the gate and looked at the car parked under
the soft drift of leaves from the trees in the avenue, and she
felt sick. Her instinct was to run and hide herself somewhere where he would never be able to find her, never be
able to hurt her again, but she steadied herself just in time.
What point was there in flight? She would have to face him
in the end.

He was not alone. She knew that even before the front
door opened at her touch, and she heard Jan's laugh ring out
from the sitting room. As if she had been waiting for the
sound of the front door, Mrs Laurence appeared in the
doorway, anxiety warring on her face with a kind of relief.

'Darling, Jan's here,' she greeted her without preamble.
'And—and she's married, Juliet. She's married an Italian.
He's here with her. Won't you come in and meet them?'

Don't let me cry, Juliet prayed, or scream, or faint. She
was amazed when she spoke to hear how calm her voice
sounded.

'I'll come in later, Mim. I'm going up to change now, and
I thought I'd do some gardening.'

'But I've made the tea. It's all ready.' Mrs Laurence took

another step out into the hall. 'Darling, it really would be better if you came in now. Please believe me . . .'

She broke off as Jan appeared in the doorway behind her. Her condition was more obvious now, and she was doing little to conceal it in an elegant maternity outfit probably designed by a top fashion house. She smiled across the hall at Juliet, as if that last painful confrontation had never taken place.

'Julie, my sweet!' She lifted a hand in greeting, and Juliet saw the massive diamond that gleamed there. Even in that moment she could still feel relief that Santino had not bestowed the ring he had given her, the ring she had left in her room before her departure, upon her sister.

'Hello, Jan.' Juliet spoke steadily. She felt as if she was bleeding to death inside, but that didn't matter just as long as she didn't give herself away. 'I hear felicitations are in order.'

Jan's smile widened. 'Indeed they are,' she drawled. 'And not before time, you might think.' She bestowed a careless kiss on her mother's cheek. 'Poor Mim! But all is forgiven, now that I'm married, isn't that so?'

Mrs Laurence turned silently and went back into the sitting room leaving the sisters facing one another. There was a long silence, then Jan said, 'Aren't you coming in? We've been waiting to have tea—and my husband wants to say hello to you.'

'That,' Juliet said very carefully, 'is a pleasure I'm going to have to forgo. Please tell him I hope you'll both be very happy.'

She turned away and made for the stairs. Santino's voice saying, 'Giulietta!' very sharply brought her up dead in her tracks, the colour draining from her face, her legs shaking.

'Oh, no!' she appealed to some unseen deity. 'Oh please, no!' She forced herself to move forward. This was her mother's house. Upstairs was her room—sanctuary.

His hand was hard on her shoulder, turning her to face him. He said in a voice throbbing with anger, 'You don't run away from me again, Giulietta.'

'Take your hands off me,' she whispered. 'If you've no consideration for me, then have some for your wife!'

She wrenched herself free and started up the stairs, her heart beating so hard she thought it would suffocate her. He was beside her, bending to scoop her off her trembling legs, carrying her up the stairs.

'Put me down!' Shame and rage battled for precedence within her. 'Don't you dare ...'

'I dare,' he said tautly. 'Once before I let you walk away from me up some stairs. I shall not make that mistake again. Which is your room?' He halted on the landing, with her in his arms. He looked down at her and the expression in his tawny eyes made her feel weak. 'Tell me, damn you!'

'It's the door at the end,' she whispered, and began to cry. He swore under his breath and strode down the landing with her. When the door was closed behind them he set her without gentleness on her feet.

'What are you doing?' she cried, scrubbing furiously at her wet cheeks with her fists like a child. 'You have no right to do this. Your *wife's* downstairs, What is she going to think? And my mother?'

He rested his hands on his hips. His glance raked her from head to foot.

'Your mother's opinion may perhaps be of concern to me,' he said. 'But I have no wife.'

'What are you saying?' She pressed her hands against her face, staring at him.

'I am saying I am not married. *Dio*, Giulietta, how many times must I say it?'

'But Jan's married. Mim said she was—to an Italian. She told me her husband was waiting to say hello.'

'And you assumed it must be me.' He smiled without

mirth. 'No, Giulietta. Your sister has found a husband—one Pietro Rizziani, whom I think I have mentioned to you once before.' She gazed up at him, her lips parting soundlessly, and he gave a sardonic nod.

'*Si cara*—that Rizziani.'

'But—I thought he was—married already,' she faltered.

'So he was—then, but he has suffered a tragic bereavement.' Santino's lips twisted cynically. 'Your sister's pregnancy persuaded him to forgo the usual decent interval before remarrying. That and the handsome dowry she was able to bring with her.'

'But Jan has no money——' she began, her voice tailing off suddenly as she realised what he had done.

He nodded. 'I do not begrudge it, *cara*,' he said. 'After all, she is almost a member of my family.'

'You mean—because she was going to marry your brother,' she said. She seemed to be having the greatest difficulty in breathing normally.

'No,' he shook his head. 'Because I am going to marry you, *amore*.'

'No.' She turned away from him towards the window.

'Oh, but yes,' he said softly. 'I have not travelled all this way to be rejected, *mia*.' He turned her to face him. For a long moment he looked down at her, and then his mouth came down on hers, harsh and bruising with a need, she realised dazedly, as great as her own. The world spun around her as she clung to him, exchanging kiss for kiss without reserve. He was murmuring endearments in his own language against her lips, his hands caressing her body, arousing and demanding but with a new and thrilling tenderness.

At last he lifted his head. His eyes were gleaming with triumph, but she did not begrudge him his victory.

'Now tell me you don't want me,' he said huskily.

'I thought you didn't want me.' The colour rose in her face.

'When did I ever not want you, *mia*?' he demanded. He smiled a little. 'Even when we first met, when I tried not to like you very much, I wanted you. Didn't you know it? You were everything I despised, and yet there you were, under my skin. Didn't you ever ask yourself why I took you to dinner that night? It wasn't at all what I intended.'

'Then what did you intend?' She let herself be drawn back against the hard warmth of his body, glorying in his response to her.

'I intended to make you give up Mario—by fair means or foul,' he told her frankly. 'I'd sent you the roses to make sure you were the right girl, and I had made my plans to take you away to the *castello* if you wouldn't see reason. What I hadn't planned was the innocence I seemed to see in your eyes. All my preconceptions went for nothing. I should have guessed then that Janina Laurence, in spite of all her pathetic stories, had a sister.'

'So you sent those roses—and I signed for them. The same name, the same initial.' She gave a little sigh. 'No wonder I couldn't convince you that I wasn't Jan.'

'And yet I should have known,' he said roughly. 'The first time I touched you—kissed you—should have told me. After all, I had sworn I would destroy you, and instead I found myself wanting to protect you. I didn't know whether to be angry with you or with myself.'

'But I still don't understand.' Her eyes searched his face. 'When you did find the truth—you made me pretend to be engaged to you—and then you were so cruel, so uncaring.'

'Cruel perhaps, *carissima*,' he said softly. 'But never uncaring.' His lips explored the line of her throat, and she heard him laugh delightedly at her instinctive quiver of response. 'That pretence engagement was all I could think of to keep you near me. I knew I had frightened you—perhaps even repelled you. I wanted a reprieve—time for us to get to know one another. I told myself to rush you into marriage would not be fair to you, but in the fullness of time I meant to tell you that the engagement was for real. As I should have done,' he added frowningly, 'but for your sister and her mischiefmaking.'

'I thought you were falling in love with her,' she confessed. 'At least, I thought you wanted her. I thought that was why you had taken her to Rome with you.'

He gave her an incredulous look. 'I took her to Rome to meet Rizziani,' he said. 'On one of my business trips I'd heard he had become a widower. Their first meeting was not quite the success I had hoped for, which was why I had to bring her back to the *castello* with me.'

'But she said—she made me think ...'

'I know what she made you think, *cara*,' he said grimly. 'Just as she made me think you were yearning to return to England to the arms of someone called Barry.'

'Oh, no, she can't have done!' Juliet stared up at him appalled. 'I mean, there was never anything—and anyway, she didn't even *know* about Barry,' she added rather incoherently.

He smiled. 'It seems your mother must have mentioned him in one of her letters.'

'But why should she tell you such a thing?'

He shrugged. 'Perhaps she thought still that I was a better matrimonial bet than Rizziani,' he said sardonically. 'I soon disabused her mind of that notion.'

'But doesn't Signor Rizziani—mind about the baby?' she asked half disbelievingly.

'Why should he?' Santino grinned faintly. 'I have it on the best authority that it is probably his.'

She stared up at him. 'But who says that?'

His grin widened. 'He does, *cara*, and so does your sister. So it must be possible, to say the least. But enough of them.'

He drew her close to him. 'When will you marry me, Giulietta? Don't make me wait too long. These past weeks have been agony.'

'And for me.' She put her hand up and stroked his cheek.

'So I should hope,' he said outrageously. 'It has been my only consolation to know that you were suffering as much as I was.'

She pulled a face at him. 'Then why didn't you come sooner?'

'For a number of reasons. I had my business to see to. I have neglected it lately, which is bad. And for a time I believed what your sister had said—that you preferred this Barry, and could not wait to get back to him.' He grimaced. 'I should have listened to my mother instead. She told me that you were unhappy when you walked out on me that day, and she told me why. It was then I realised what the *bella* Janina had been up to, and I bullied the truth out of her about you and this Barry.' He shook his head. 'It was then, I think, that she decided her safest course was to settle for Rizziani.'

'Your mother.' Juliet was troubled. 'Does she know—that you've come to ask me to marry you?'

'Of course she knows,' he said impatiently. 'She is waiting to welcome you as her *nuora*. Mario and Francesca are to be married at the end of the month and she hopes that you will attend the wedding in any case.'

'I should love to.' Juliet's eyes lit up. 'That is if I can get the time off from school,' she added. 'And I shall have to give my notice in right away if I want to leave at Christmas.'

'What is this notice?' Santino was suddenly at his most arrogant. 'I want you with me now, *cara*, not when some employer gives you leave. Leave it to me. I shall arrange everything.'

'I wish I could,' she said ruefully. 'But I shall have to leave in the proper manner. I have the children to consider

—and the other staff. I can't leave them in the lurch.' She ventured a look at him and saw he was frowning. 'Don't you understand?'

'I understand,' he said a little bleakly. 'I understand that I must learn patience, *mia cara*, which will not be an easy lesson for me. But no matter.' The frown lifted and the tawny eyes slid over her, shadowed with desire. 'I shall use the time of waiting to plan some lessons of my own to teach you, my beautiful one,' he murmured. 'You have taught me to love you. *Bene*. I shall teach you how to receive love. I'll teach you to want me as much as I want you.'

'I've learned that already,' she whispered, lifting her face for his kiss, trembling as he drew her closer still against him.

'And if I asked you to prove it?' he said almost roughly, then swore under his breath. 'No—forgive me, *cara*, I've said that I'll be patient. Perhaps it would be easier and safer if we were to get out of this bedroom and go downstairs to drink your mother's tea. But first'—he reached into his pocket—'we'll put this back where it belongs.'

Gently he slid the emerald ring on to her finger, then raised her hand to his lips.

'No pretence this time, *cara*,' he told her huskily. 'No pretence ever again. This'—his arms went around her, demandingly, possessively—'this is the only reality, and it is ours for the rest of our lives.'

The Warrender Saga

The most frequently requested series of Harlequin Romances . . . Mary Burchell's Warrender Saga

A Song Begins   The Curtain Rises
The Broken Wing   Song Cycle
Child of Music   Music of the Heart
Unbidden Melody
Remembered Serenade
When Love Is Blind

Each complete novel is set in the exciting world of
music and opera, spanning the years from the
meeting of Oscar and Anthea in *A Song Begins* to
his knighthood in *Remembered Serenade*. These
nine captivating love stories introduce you to a cast
of characters as vivid, interesting and delightful as
the glittering, exotic locations. From the tranquil
English countryside to the capitals of Europe—
London, Paris, Amsterdam—the Warrender Saga
will sweep you along in an unforgettable journey of
drama, excitement and romance.

Complete and mail this coupon today!

Harlequin Reader Service

In U.S.A.
MPO Box 707
Niagara Falls, NY 14302

In Canada
Harlequin Reader Service
Stratford, Ontario N5A 6W2

Please send me the following editions of The Warrender Saga.
I am enclosing my check or money order for $1.25 per novel
ordered, plus 49¢ to cover postage and handling.

☐ 980 A Song Begins
☐ 1100 The Broken Wing
☐ 1244 When Love Is Blind
☐ 1405 The Curtain Rises

☐ 1508 Child of Music
☐ 1587 Music of the Heart
☐ 1767 Unbidden Melody
☐ 1834 Song Cycle

☐ 1936 Remembered Serenade

BONUS OFFER — *We Followed Our Stars*, Mary Burchell's
moving autobiography, is yours ABSOLUTELY FREE when
you purchase all nine Warrender Saga novels.
☐ Yes, I have purchased all nine of the above. Please send me
   my copy of *We Followed Our Stars*.

Number of novels checked _____ @ $1.25 each = $ _____

We Followed Our Stars
Mary Burchell's autobiography _____ x $1.50 $ _____

Postage and handling $ _____.49

New York State and New Jersey residents please
add appropriate sales tax $ _____

                              TOTAL $ _____

NAME _____
                    (Please Print)
ADDRESS _____

CITY _____

STATE/PROV _____ ZIP/POSTAL CODE _____

Offer Expires December 31, 1979

PRS 307

Remember when a good love story made you feel like holding hands?

The wonder of love is timeless.
Once discovered, love remains,
despite the passage of time.
Harlequin brings you stories of
true love, about women the
world over – women like you.

Harlequin Romances
with the
Harlequin magic...

Recapture the sparkle of first
love...relive the joy of true
romance...enjoy these stories
of love today.

Six new novels every month –
wherever paperbacks
are sold.